THE COLUMBIA
RIVER TREATY

A Primer

by Robert William Sandford,

Deborah Harford and Jon O'Riordan

Rocky Mountain Books
www.rmbooks.com

Library and Archives Canada Cataloguing in Publication

Sandford, Robert W., author
      The Columbia River Treaty : a primer / by Robert William Sandford,
Deborah Harford and Jon O'Riordan.

Includes bibliographical references.
Issued in print and electronic formats.
ISBN 978-1-77160-042-2 (bound).—ISBN 978-1-77160-043-9 (html).—
ISBN 978-1-77160-044-6 (pdf)

      1. Columbia River Treaty (1961 January 17). 2. Water resources development—
Law and legislation—Columbia River Watershed. 3. Water resources development—
Social aspects—Columbia River Watershed. 4. Water resources development—
Environmental aspects—Columbia River Watershed. I. Harford, Deborah, author
II. O'Riordan, Jon, author III. Title.

HD1694.A2S25 2014   333.91'13097116   C2014-904029-6
                           C2014-904030-X

Printed in Canada

Rocky Mountain Books acknowledges the financial support for its publishing
program from the Government of Canada through the Canada Book Fund (CBF) and
the Canada Council for the Arts, and from the province of British Columbia through
the British Columbia Arts Council and the Book Publishing Tax Credit.

 Canadian Heritage Patrimoine canadien   Canada Council for the Arts Conseil des Arts du Canada

 BRITISH COLUMBIA ARTS COUNCIL
Supported by the Province of British Columbia

The interior pages of this book have been produced on 100% post-consumer recycled
paper, processed chlorine free and printed with vegetable-based dyes.

MIX
Paper from
responsible sources
FSC® C016245
www.fsc.org

For those who were not treated fairly, equitably or with dignity on and after September 16, 1964.

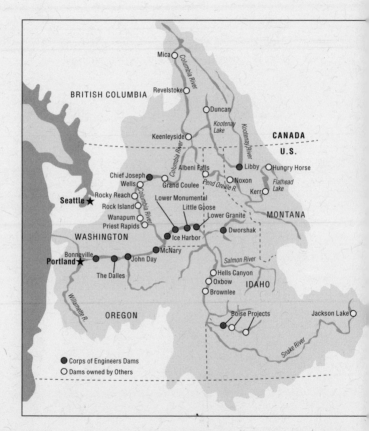

Contents

The intent of the Columbia River Treaty and its
success to date
> This chapter outlines the initial intent of the Treaty,
> focusing on flood protection and hydro power gen-
> eration. It explains how the limited scope of the
> Treaty enabled it to be very successful in meeting
> expectations of the two signatories.

Success at what cost?
> This chapter explains how elements related to social
> impacts and environmental concerns, particularly

the importance of protecting fish and fish habitat, were not addressed in the original Treaty. The chapter also demonstrates how these issues have become more important over the last half century, championed by a new set of actors on both sides of the border, including Canadian First Nations and US tribes.

This chapter outlines what has changed in the larger world and in the basin since the Columbia River Treaty was ratified in 1964. It demonstrates how the upcoming treaty renegotiations could be influenced by different social norms associated with equity and social justice; by new views on the relevance of traditional and local knowledge; by evolving perspectives on ecological dynamics; and by a changing hydrology.

This chapter introduces economic information that demonstrates the relative values associated with

flood control, energy, fisheries, ecosystems and ag-
riculture. It concludes by proposing that these val-
ues are significant enough to influence the new
treaty arrangements, particularly in view of the
changing hydrology over the next 60 years.

Chapter Five   105
What are the prospects for renegotiating the
Treaty?

This chapter identifies the differences in perspective
that exist at the time of this writing within Canada
and between Canada and the United States with
respect to the benefits associated with the Treaty. It
then suggests options for including new values into
current and future Treaty negotiations.

Chapter Six   127
What's next?

This chapter outlines the established course of for-
mal negotiation between the legal entities respon-
sible for the Treaty. It is intended to show read-
ers how they may engage with these issues or make
their wishes known politically regarding the out-
come of negotiations. It also outlines additional

scientific data-modelling analyses that will be re-quired in order to refine our understanding of the effects of a changing hydrology on Treaty values.

Acknowledgements

The authors wish to acknowledge the support of the advisory board for Simon Fraser University's Adaptation to Climate Change Team (ACT), in particular Dr. Nancy Olewiler, director of the School of Public Policy at Simon Fraser, and Dr. Stewart Cohen, senior researcher with Environment Canada and adjunct professor of forest resources management at the University of British Columbia. These experts have offered wise advice, astute scientific perspectives and valuable direction to all who have been involved in our work on reconsideration of the Columbia River Treaty from the point of view of climate change adaptation.

We are also grateful for the hard work and dedication of economist and ACT researcher Joyce Yuan, who covered a great deal of new ground in efforts to estimate the past, present and future value prosperity in every region through which the river passes.

The river's mighty course, and the timeline of the Treaty created to harness its power, could be seen as a symbol of the extraordinary growth North American society has enjoyed over the past 50 years. But it also tracks the emergence of unprecedented challenges, due in part to that very success and its consequences – challenges that must now be taken into account as the Treaty comes due for reconsideration, its future inextricably linked with that of the river.

The benefits of the Treaty under its original terms are well defined. Large-scale control of the Columbia River's massive cross-border flow of an average 2800 cubic metres per second from its 103,000-square-kilometre drainage basin in Canada has prevented billions of dollars in flood damage. It has also created, as mentioned earlier, the largest hydro power generating project in North America, providing almost carbon-free, renewable energy to millions of people. This harnessing of the river's enormous flow has bestowed many additional benefits, including safe navigation for river traffic worth billions of dollars (while also contributing to the reduction of emissions by diminishing road and rail traffic), massive recreation areas around reservoirs, and guaranteed irrigation for an agriculture sector worth $5-billion in Washington State alone. The agreement is a valuable one: in return for dam construction and maintenance, British Columbia receives an annual payment known as the Canadian Entitlement in the form of hydro power revenue from the US, which at $100-million to $300-million a year represents a valued contribution to the province's general revenue.

Although the Treaty has no expiry date, 2024 is enshrined in it as the first possible year in which either party may terminate the agreement after having given the other party a mandatory minimum of 10 years' notice. This is why 2014 is an important year. At the time of this writing, the sovereign parties on both sides of the border are actively considering their options as well as the benefits that have been enjoyed and the challenges that have emerged. There is much to consider today that did not occur to the Treaty's architects in the expansion-oriented world of the 1960s. For instance, Canada's First Nations and the US indigenous tribes now have voices, rights and representation that were absent or unasserted at the time of the Treaty's signing. They share common interests in a variety of issues ranging from the presence and health of salmon in the river, to restitution for injustices suffered, to the security and preservation of sacred sites that were inundated by the new dams. Columbia basin residents in BC and the US also share concerns about quality of life and the integrity of the ecosystems they rely on for recreation, livelihood and community well-being.

Issues such as the changing values of agriculture, the economic link between water, energy and the needs of ecosystems and species, and climate change require new capacity to respond under an agreement that was not created to consider such factors. As the sovereign parties to the Treaty marshal their initial positions, one of their challenges is to look forward into the "new normal" we face in a changing climate. The effects of climate change on weather patterns are projected to affect the hydrology of the Columbia basin, increasing the risk of severe flooding and extended drought, which in turn will impact both hydro power production and the vitality of the ecosystems and species that depend on the river's flow. The Treaty's signatories must therefore attempt to prepare a new agreement that meets the historical goals of the original while laying the groundwork for a path forward that will protect and sustain the river and its inhabitants – human and otherwise – for generations to come.

Our species has a unique ability – what we might call our "adaptive advantage" – to prepare relatively quickly to adjust to changing conditions such as the risks posed by climate change. We have learned how to predict future conditions using increasingly advanced climate modelling techniques. We have also begun developing expertise in the complex policy, planning and implementation approaches required for responding to such risks. With this knowledge, we have the potential to plan in such a way that we can avoid or at least minimize future damage, and optimize our ability to benefit from coming trends where we might otherwise be vulnerable. Our ability to assess future climate change impacts and ways of managing them will play a crucial role in the consideration of priorities in a renewed Columbia River Treaty. We ignore these things at our peril.

This primer sets out the history of the Treaty and its mechanisms; discusses the success of its original goals and their eventual shortcomings; identifies challenges posed by climate change and population growth in the basin; discusses future values for the flows; identifies strengths and weaknesses in the current mechanisms, both legal and infrastructural; considers precedents being set in transboundary agreements elsewhere in the world; and explores key actions the sovereign parties might consider as they attempt to represent future generations and exercise the "adaptive advantage" in the results they produce by 2024.

While it is not compulsory for changes to be made in 2024 – that year is just the first opportunity – our growing populations and the changing nature of the climate suggest we would be wise to be proactive.

Chapter One
THE INTENT OF THE COLUMBIA RIVER TREATY AND ITS SUCCESS TO DATE

After the Second World War a wave of large-scale infrastructure projects swept the US as ambitions soared and a golden era in American capitalism bloomed. Empowered by strong industry, a burgeoning economy, maturing war bonds and a reliable, educated workforce resulting from the GI Bill, the US government embarked on a massive quest for economic expansion. Canada experienced similar industrial empowerment, enjoying an economic boom as the investments in manufacturing that had been made in support of the war effort transformed into vigorous post-war production with growing export capacity. The two neighbouring countries, keenly aware of the increasing demand for energy and full of enthusiasm for the potential for expansion, had begun as early as 1944 to discuss collaboration for the purpose of creating new hydroelectric power reserves on the Columbia River.

The Columbia is the fourth-largest watercourse on the continent, exceeded only by the Mississippi, the Mackenzie and the St. Lawrence. The great river rises in British Columbia, Canada, though only 15 per cent of the total extent of its basin is found there. Its headwaters are high in the Canadian Rockies, in Columbia Lake, Lake Windermere and the Columbia Wetlands, flanked by the BC Rockies and the Purcell Range. These mountains' generous snowpacks and BC's rainy climate are the reason why the province's portion of the basin contributes 30 to 35 per cent of the river's entire flow, including its flood potential. Floodwaters at Portland, Oregon, are 50 per cent Canadian. British Columbia also has most of the best water storage sites due to its sparsely populated interior, deep valleys and vast geographic expanse. Optimum sites for hydro power generation, however, are mostly in the US, due to less-steep terrain and other factors such as proximity to markets.

A transboundary collaboration for mutual benefit was therefore a logical move, but such international agreements are time-consuming to negotiate. It took many years to draft and ratify the Columbia Treaty – a fact that is not lost on the signatories today as they consider their options. Terminating the Treaty would very likely end all possibility of remaking such an arrangement, given the vastly expanded range of issues and interests in terms of population, industry, ecosystems and community governance. We discuss this and other considerations regarding next steps in chapter 6.

Canada and the US had created the International Joint Commission (IJC) in 1909 to address mutual use of trans-border waters as part of the Boundary Waters Treaty implemented that year. In 1944, to open the investigation into the potential for collaboration over the Columbia, the two countries asked the IJC to study the potential of the river system as a resource for development of seven key factors: domestic water supply, navigation, hydro power, flood control, irrigation, reclamation of wetlands and conservation of fish and wildlife – plus any other beneficial public purposes that might be identified.

It was amid this optimistic and ambitious

atmosphere that the Columbia River flooded in 1948, causing catastrophic damage on both sides of the border, from its headwaters in the Canadian Rockies to its mouth on the US Pacific coast. Worst hit was Vanport City, Oregon, the state's second-largest town at the time, the brainchild of industrial magnate Henry Kaiser.

Constructed only six years earlier, in 1942, Vanport City was intended to house the thousands of shipyard workers Kaiser was bringing in by rail in response to the war effort. Showing a level of ignorance of flood risks that is still evident among some municipal planners today, Kaiser had the city constructed in the floodplain, protected by levees and dikes, about 15 feet below the river's level at its lowest point.

The spring of 1948 was unseasonably warm and the previous winter had built up a larger than usual snowpack. The rapid melt that resulted filled both the Columbia and the Willamette rivers to well above flood stage. On May 30 a major dike gave way and 10 feet of water surged through the town. The number of deaths reported varies, depending on the account, from 16 to 50. Vanport's peak population of 40,000 had shrunk by the war's end, but an influx of returning veterans had maintained the city's numbers at about 18,500 residents. What is certain is that all homes were ruined beyond repair, rendering the entire town uninhabitable. Washington State too saw flooding, in the towns of Kennewick and Richland, with only one fatality but $50-million in damage. Homes and farms were affected all the way downstream through BC and Washington to the river's mouth at Astoria, Oregon.

The dramatic, overnight destruction of Vanport and the widespread inundation to an extent not seen since the Great Flood of 1894 brought Canada and the US together with an even stronger motivation to find solutions on a grand scale to both the flood issue and the need for additional power. The US Flood Control Act of 1950 created the Columbia River Flood Control System with provision for transboundary basin management, but it was not until 1959 that an agreement between Canada and the US finally materialized. As we will see in a moment, had it been up to W.A.C. Bennett, BC's premier from 1952 to 1972, collaborative hydro power generation on the Columbia could have happened as early as 1954, driven by the province alone without involving Ottawa.

However, as has always been the case historically in the constitutional crazy quilt of overlapping jurisdictions that is Canada, most public-policy issues of any consequence have both a federal and a provincial aspect to them. The national interest lay in supporting the overall economic and population growth of the country, while Bennett considered regional resource development a high priority. Although ultimately resolved, the competing interests in the same resource between the two levels of government culminated in some political tension in 1954 when Bennett proposed an agreement with a private US company to build a dam on the Columbia in BC to facilitate US hydro power generation. The initiative was promptly quashed the following year when Ottawa enacted legislation requiring a federal licence to make any modifications to the flows of an international river.

In 1959 the International Columbia River Engineering Board made a report to the IJC in the form of an appraisal focused on the potential for development of hydro power, with additional consideration given to how the system could be modified for flood control and other benefits, concluding that such a project was both practical and desirable for both parties. Canadian international-law scholar C.B. Bourne's contribution to this work played a significant role in getting the US to admit that Canada might have an enforceable interest in the river under a principle of "absolute sovereignty" which the US itself had asserted decades earlier. Called the Harmon Doctrine, the principle was named after a US Attorney General in the 1890s who claimed Mexico had no right to any water originating in the US, even if the river flows into Mexico. Water policy expert Peter Gleick notes that this doctrine, which says that "upstream water users have the right to do whatever they want with the water in their own 'territory' no matter what harm it causes to downstream users," has been "universally repudiated: in international law, in US law and in any ethical or moral set of rules." The Columbia River Treaty, however, was constructed to ensure that the agreement, as between the sovereign parties at least, was an equitable one.

Later in 1959 the IJC produced a set of recommendations for the sovereign parties, outlining key principles for identifying and allocating the benefits that would result from the co-operative use of storage for the primary purposes of power generation and flood control. The report outlined three alternative plans, each of which required different valleys to be flooded for storage. It also stated that any other benefits of the agreement would be so much less valuable than the two main objectives that it was not necessary to formulate principles for their governance in the Treaty context.

The report thus failed to acknowledge a number of key issues that are very much at the forefront of today's discussions. For one thing, it did not characterize the implications of inundation for reservoir development of areas that held high value for Canadian residents of the basin. Neither did it consider the negative impacts on fish and wildlife that would result from dam construction and the necessity for manipulation of reservoir levels to achieve reliable flood control. The report also ignored the spiritual value that Canadian First Nations and US tribes place on the presence of salmon, the passage of which had been blocked by the Grand Coulee dam 26 years earlier but whose return the indigenous people nevertheless hoped for, as they still do today. There was also the issue of the integrity of sacred sites that would be inundated by reservoirs, as well as the overall effect on the entire basin ecosystem, which local First Nations see as a unitary whole in their creation stories. The report also underestimated the extraordinarily high value of irrigation and flow regulation that led to development of a $5-billion agriculture industry in Washington State, while Canadian agricultural land was lost to the creation of reservoirs.

The IJC report formally kicked off negotiations between the two countries, which began on February 11, 1960, to identify Treaty dam sites and deal with details as to construction and joint use. On January 17, 1961, Prime Minister John Diefenbaker and President Dwight Eisenhower signed the Treaty.

Much more work was required, of course, not only to codify myriad details such as the signatories' specific technical operating agencies (called "entities," one Canadian, one US), but also to reconcile Canadian national and provincial interests. Premier Bennett was concerned about the cost, both in financial and in local environmental terms, of the provincial requirement to build three dams, given that BC's small population at the time did not need the additional 50 per cent of Treaty hydro power – the Canadian Entitlement – that the US would owe to Canada under the agreement. This issue was eventually resolved when a consortium of 37 public and four private utilities in the US agreed to pay C$254-million to purchase the Canadian Entitlement for a 30-year period from the completion date of the new Canadian dams. Canada, via BC, was also to receive $64.4-million as 50 per cent of the estimated worth of projected future US flood damage prevented from 1968 through 2024. The combination of these two amounts would fund construction and maintenance of the three new BC dams.

On July 8, 1963, the two Canadian authorities signed the Canada–British Columbia Agreement, transferring "all proprietary rights, title and interests arising under the Treaty" to British Columbia and naming BC Hydro as the Canadian entity responsible for managing the daily operations of the reservoirs and hydroelectric facilities that would be built. (Hydro's US operational counterparts, the Bonneville Power Administration and the US Army Corps of Engineers, were not constituted as the US entity until September 1964, soon after the Treaty was ratified.) A supplement to the main Canada–BC agreement was signed January

13, 1964, resolving final details governing Treaty authority, benefits and responsibility.

The Columbia River Treaty and a Protocol clarifying certain Treaty terms were formally ratified by Prime Minister Lester Pearson, Premier W.A.C. Bennett and President Lyndon Johnson at the international boundary at Blaine, Washington, and Douglas, BC, on September 16, 1964.

TREATY TERMS AND CONDITIONS

In order to optimize flood management and power generation, the Treaty mandated construction of three new dams in BC and one in the US, accompanied by coordinated operation and management of reservoirs and water flows. Between 1967 and 1973, BC Hydro constructed 15.5 million acre-feet (Maf)* of reservoir storage in all, comprised

---

* An acre foot is a unit derived from irrigation agriculture. It refers to the amount of water required to cover one acre (66 feet by 660 feet) of flat land to a depth of one foot. This is a volume equal to about 325,851 US gallons, which amounts to about 43,560 cubic feet, or 1233.5 cubic metres. A volume of 1 Maf is equivalent to 1.23 cubic kilometres, or roughly the entire 230-kilometre length of the Arrow Lakes reservoir to a depth of about 2.4 metres.

of 7 Maf behind the Mica dam, 7.1 at the Hugh Keenleyside (originally called the High Arrow dam) and 1.4 at Duncan, while the US built the Libby dam in Montana with a reservoir capacity of 5.8 Maf.

The twin Treaty goals of flood protection and hydro power generation were reflected in payments that went directly to BC under the terms of the Canada–British Columbia Agreement.

TREATY BENEFITS

Flood control

As described above (see page 16), the US paid Canada $64.4-million to provide 8.45 Maf of flood storage under a plan that specified guaranteed reservoir levels and capacity as well as additional storage on an on-call basis which had not yet been used. There is an extra 0.5 Maf available that was not paid for, however. The amount paid represented half the estimated value of the damage that would be avoided by Treaty flood control over the period from 1968 through 2024. This estimate proved to be shortsighted. Due to population growth, urban development and agricultural expansion – all of which were made possible by the Treaty's success – the actual worth of the flood control Canada has provided to date is considerably more than this amount. Canadian residents of Trail and Castlegar have also benefited from flood protection created by the Treaty reservoirs.

Hydro power

The Columbia produces the most hydroelectric power of any river in North America. The US, with its larger population and economy, placed an initially higher value on developing hydro power facilities than did Canada. Premier Bennett did, however, have a hydro power vision for the province. His "Two Rivers" policy envisioned development of the hydroelectric potential of both the Peace and the Columbia rivers. The policy began to be realized with construction of the W.A.C. Bennett dam on the Peace beginning in 1961, concurrently with the Hugh Keenleyside dam on the Columbia, and with the ratification of the Columbia River Treaty in 1964. The nationalization of BC Electric as the Crown corporation BC Hydro in 1961, can also be attributed to this policy.

Under the CRT, Canada manages 15.5 Maf of its

Treaty dam storage for optimum power generation downstream in BC and the US. This arrangement provides approximately 44 per cent of the electricity that BC Hydro delivers in British Columbia. However, storage regulation in Canada provides additional power potential in the US, and the Treaty entitled British Columbia to be paid for 50 per cent of the value of this incremental power. In 1968 the US purchased the first 30 years of the Canadian Entitlement for $254-million. However, since 1998 when this arrangement ended, Canada has been receiving the current value of the power produced annually, now worth $100-million to $300-million per year – an amount similar to what the US paid for the entire first 30 years. BC Hydro receives the benefit in the form of power returned by its US counterpart, the Bonneville Power Administration, delivered according to daily schedules set by BC Hydro. The province then sells this power, with the proceeds going into general revenues. Just as the US now saves millions annually due to the safety afforded by Treaty-driven flood control, the value of the power produced has mushroomed because of population and industry growth as well as increases in the price of electricity, especially that produced from renewable sources.

COLUMBIA BASIN TRUST

As outlined earlier, the IJC's assessment of the value of the Treaty failed to characterize the losses that would be experienced by BC residents of the basin who would see vast areas of their beloved region permanently inundated by reservoir storage. They would also have to deal with the side-effects of continual adjustment of water levels, such as dust storms during periods of drawdown in preparation for potential floodwaters, and disruption of seasonal patterns of wildlife species behaviour. About 2,000 residents lost their homes and farms to the Treaty dams and were obliged to relocate and develop new livelihoods. Dissatisfaction with both these historical injustices and ongoing inconveniences (discussed in chapter 2), came to a head in 1992, when local governments joined forces to create the Columbia River Treaty Committee to work with the local electorate to negotiate compensation from the province.

The result was the formation of the Columbia

Basin Trust (CBT) in 1995, governed by a board of basin residents, and the establishment of ongoing payments to the region, by way of the trust, of a portion of the benefits generated by the Treaty. This funding consisted of a one-time endowment of $321-million, plus $32-million in 16 annual instalments of $2-million, the last of which was paid in 2010.

A further $250-million went to the Columbia Power Corporation, the CBT's joint venture partner in power projects in the basin, which include the Arrow Lakes generating station, the Brilliant dam, the Brilliant expansion project and the Waneta expansion project. Fifty per cent of the net profits from increased power production from these facilities goes to the CBT for the social, economic and environmental benefit of the people of the basin. Initiatives include community development, water and environment projects, economic development and social and youth programs. In 2012–2013, CBT disbursed over $18-million in benefits and had $25-million in total revenues. Those annual amounts are projected to rise to $25-million and $33-million respectively by 2015–2016, when the Waneta expansion begins to produce power.

"CALLED UPON" FLOOD CONTROL

As discussed, 2024 is enshrined in the Treaty as the first opportunity for termination of the agreement, with a mandatory minimum 10-year notice period. It is up to the signatories whether or not they exercise this opportunity, although Canada cannot terminate the Treaty without BC's consent, per the 1963 Canada–BC Agreement. However, there is one major change that does occur in 2024: a shift to "called upon" flood control. Under this provision, the rental agreement for flood storage space behind Canadian Treaty dams expires, allowing BC to operate Canadian reservoirs primarily for power production. Outcomes for the US would be complex, as that country would be required to regulate its own storages for flood control and could not "call upon" additional storage in Canada until it had already carried out this regulation and still the potential for flooding downstream remained. For example, the Arrow Lakes Reservoir is key for US flood control because it is the closest storage to the lower Columbia. With the onset of called upon flood control, BC would not be required to keep this reservoir drawn down to accommodate excess water bound for the US except in such an emergency, and could therefore generally maintain it at a higher, more stable level that would benefit local residents and ecosystems.

A further issue is the cost of upgrading infrastructure as the dams' lifespans come to an end. The US paid for the initial flood storage agreement as partial contribution to dam construction, but there is no provision for further costs after that agreement expires. In other words, the US flood storage agreement applies only to the construction cost of the dams it helped build, not to the upgrades that will be necessary as the dams age and approach the end of their designed lifespans. However, not all dam maintenance is necessarily linked to the Treaty, since some of those costs relate to domestic safety and power needs. Thus the matter of future infrastructure maintenance costs is a potential area for negotiation.

THE TREATY TODAY

Over the past 50 years, the Columbia River Treaty has – at least in terms of its narrowly stated goals – been an enormous success. Billions of dollars have been generated in hydro power used by Canada and the US; billions of dollars have been saved in flood damage. The revenue from the arrangement has earned significant income for US power utilities, the province of BC and more recently the BC residents of the Columbia basin. The human urge to harness the power of nature for our own benefit has paid off handsomely based on the terms agreed upon by the ratifying authorities in 1964.

Fifty years later, however, in 2014, the Treaty is operating in a world in which priorities have changed, and those terms – a limited focus on hydro power and flood control – are now being revisited. In fact, the timeframe of the Columbia River Treaty provides extraordinary insight into the trajectory of social and industrial development over the past half-century. In that time, we have developed a new awareness of the rights of indigenous peoples; of the mounting global pressure on fresh water availability; of the implications of that pressure for ecosystem health, food security and the need for renewable energy sources; and of the changing values of all of these things in the context of the threats posed by climate change. These changing realities demand that, if we are to renew the Treaty in 2024 and think 60 years ahead as our predecessors did, we will have to take into account climate models that project significant changes in streamflow and snowpack, as well as ecosystem and species range shifts and stresses. We will have to consider the implications of a "carbon budget" – the amount of carbon left that we can "safely" burn before switching to emissions-free fuels – and the likelihood of a global food crisis. We discuss these considerations in chapters 4 and 5.

Before we look forward, however, we must take stock of the costs of the Treaty's success to date. Having acknowledged the triumph of this historic collaboration between two countries as they entered a new atmosphere of optimism and growth following the horrors of the Second World War, we turn to the details that were overlooked, unforeseen or simply ignored in order to achieve this monumental feat of engineering. We should note, however, before exploring these costs in chapter 2, that a number of adjustments have been made to Treaty agreements and operational practices designed to offset to a certain extent some of the more significant impacts the original Treaty has had on ecosystems. These measures, discussed in more detail in chapter 5, include the following:

- the Northwest Power Act of 1980, which represented the first recognition of fish flows to meet endangered species legislation;
- the Non-Treaty Storage Agreements, frequently revised, which provide for additional flows across the border during dry years to assist fisheries;
- the 2004 Columbia River Water Use Plan, which defines how BC Hydro operates its facilities in relation to all known water use interests on the Columbia River;
- BC Hydro's Duncan Dam water use plan;
- the 1980 establishment of the US Northwest Power and Conservation Council, which updates its fish and wildlife plan every five years with the goal of rebalancing power and ecosystem management; and
- the Columbia Basin Fish and Wildlife Compensation Program (which applies only to the Canadian portion of the river).

These measures were significant in their

recognition and mitigation of some of the challenges caused by the Treaty, and have been effective in improving aspects of ecosystem management. However, the changing climate and increasing need for electricity and water allocation require further study that acknowledges the holistic nature of the basin's ecosystem needs.

Chapter Two
SUCCESS AT WHAT COST?

The task now facing the Treaty parties – that of assessing whether and how the pact should be modified as it reaches its 50th anniversary – presents complex challenges for a number of key reasons. Much has changed socially, politically, economically and environmentally. Attitudes have shifted. Lessons have been learned, mistakes revealed and new urgencies identified. The undeniable effectiveness of the Treaty in addressing flood control and hydro power must now be reconsidered in light of the social impacts and environmental concerns that have arisen as significant priorities in the past half-century and that were passed over by the IJC in its 1959 report.

There are several significant changes informing these new priorities. Impacts on the environment – particularly fish and fish habitat – stemming from the active management of reservoir levels are better understood. Parties that were marginalized during the Treaty's establishment, such as First Nations and local citizenry, are now empowered and expect the right to be heard. The growing influence of climate change on river levels – with extremes forecast for both drought and flood – requires careful attention and planning. In order to understand the pressures faced by the Treaty signatories as 2024 approaches, we must take a look back at the costs of success that resulted as the Treaty was implemented and operated.

LOST LAND AND LIVELIHOODS

In order to construct the Treaty dams and reservoirs, BC permanently flooded a total of 110,000 hectares, resulting in the loss of 3200 hectares of fertile agricultural land and 42,000 hectares of forest in the Kootenays, as well as displacement of a dozen small communities in which about 2,000 people lost their homes, primarily in the Arrow Lakes and Koocanusa reservoir regions – a somewhat ironic outcome given that this was done for the purpose of protecting US communities downstream from flooding. Four valleys were inundated, including the area underneath Koocanusa Lake, which was created by the Libby Dam in the US and extends 140 kilometres upriver, 68 kilometres of which is in BC.

Orchards, dairy farms and other valuable real estate disappeared beneath the reservoirs, while in the US the now more reliable flows expanded the irrigation and agricultural development made possible decades earlier by the completion of the Grand Coulee Dam and Lake Roosevelt. The fertile land lost to BC basin residents meant the disappearance of a significant local food security resource, while highly productive US farms and orchards in the southern portion of the basin proceeded to out-compete their BC counterparts. US agricultural subsidies served to consolidate this advantage. Ongoing discontent in the Kootenays stems from a variety of such grievances. BC residents along the Columbia tend to resent the benefits enjoyed by the US, because in general those benefits seem to result from the exact opposite in their region. The constant adjustment of BC reservoir levels to accommodate US needs for electricity, fisheries, riverfront properties, irrigation and navigation has a variety of unpleasant side effects, including soil erosion, dust storms, an increase in rainfall and winter fog, floating debris, proliferation of insects, disturbances to birds and other wildlife populations and diminished presence of fish. Beaches created by the reservoirs that might be attractive for residents and tourists are inundated during the summer months due to storage of snowmelt.

Collection of water in the reservoirs under the flood storage agreement also presents issues for locals. Some BC basin homeowners, for instance, experienced costly property damage in 2012 due to high water in the Arrow Lakes reservoir during spring runoff. At 440.5 metres (1,445.2 feet) above sea level, the water overtopped the maximum 440.13 metres (1,444 feet) allowable under the Treaty, feeding local fears that further damage may be caused in the future.

FISH AND FISH HABITAT

The mindset of the era when the Treaty was ratified tended to consider nature as a set of tools that was put on earth for humanity to use. Making policy for the health and protection of ecosystems and species was not a priority, as we have seen. The construction of the Treaty dams and reservoirs in the Kootenays significantly affected the aquatic and terrestrial species of the region, since a large amount of ecologically significant terrain is now permanently underwater.

The dams altered annual flow patterns and floodplains and disrupted ecosystem development dynamics and food chain links. Reservoir levels are manipulated year round, rising and falling by up to 12 metres at the Arrow Lakes, 25 metres at Koocanusa and 30 metres at the Duncan and Kinbasket reservoirs in order to facilitate floodwater storage and power generation. Effects on fish, wildlife and riparian ecosystems are numerous and hard to manage, with species such as sturgeon, burbot, kokanee, rainbow trout and Dolly Varden all showing signs of negative influences. Spawning areas, for instance, often located in alluvial fans where the river spreads out, are now deep underwater during spawning season. Most local fish species need shallow reaches to spawn in, except for kokanee, which require deeper water.

Historically, about one million salmon and

steelhead trout used to swim upstream to the upper Columbia annually. Since 1942, however, their passage to the BC portion of the basin has been blocked by the US's enormous Grand Coulee dam. This massive loss had a major impact on ecosystems around spawning grounds, where nutrients from decomposing fish bodies once fostered healthy plant growth and provided food for such species as grizzly bears and eagles.

Other major consequences include loss of habitat for other key stages of fish life cycles, nutrient losses, changes in flow regimes and water quality/turbidity, habitat and population fragmentation, and entrainment – the effect on fish of the artificial flows created by the dams, which may sweep large numbers downstream. A few species may have benefited from reservoir establishment in some situations, but the impacts outweigh the benefits.

Fish are not the only species affected. Those hardest hit by habitat changes and losses include wetland and riverbank dwellers such as amphibians, water birds, waders, songbirds, bats and aerial insectivores. The dams and reservoirs have had an impact on seasonal migrations, genetic exchange, predator/prey relationships, reproduction and dispersal. All these effects can and do travel, extending into areas downstream of dams and reservoirs.

Supplementary binational agreements added to the Treaty, such as those mentioned at the end of chapter 1, have helped to offset some of these consequences by diminishing flows and smoothing their variability in the spring melt season and augmenting flows during late summer and in dry periods when fish survival is threatened. As climate change progresses, with more potential for heat extremes and drought in the lower part of the basin, such flexible international collaboration will become increasingly important.

INDIGENOUS PEOPLES

The creation myth of the Ktunaxa in BC and of the Salish and Kootenai in the US recounts the racing of a water monster round and round the entire Columbia basin in a trajectory that predated by thousands of years the establishment of the "international border." Sadly, however, another feature of the predominantly European mindset during the time of the Treaty's establishment was the tendency to marginalize First Nations and tribes and insist that the border between the two countries divide them from one another. In the minds of the 1960s Treaty-makers, indigenous interests were non-existent, with catastrophic consequences. In the words of one tribal leader, "In the establishment of flood control, a permanent flood of Biblical proportions was created." In that flood, 10,000 years of aboriginal culture was lost. The Sinixt Nation was declared extinct as an entity under the Indian Act. Many sacred sites such as burial grounds remain inundated by the Treaty's reservoirs, a fact that continues to aggravate old wounds as water levels rise and fall, periodically re-exposing the ancient sites, many of which have been looted and despoiled as a result.

Salmon are sacred to indigenous people on both sides of the border. This ancient relationship reflects the iconic fish's role as an essential spoke in the wheel of life of the great forest ecosystems that make up BC's and the Pacific Northwest's extraordinary natural heritage. The loss of salmon had deeply painful consequences for the region's First Nations and tribes, for whom the fish is essential both to everyday life and to spiritual health, identity and ceremony. They continue to mourn the salmon's absence and experience negative cultural and spiritual impacts as a result.

Thus the BC First Nations and US tribes, while in different political positions due to the asymmetry of sovereign-government agreements in the two countries, share common concerns regarding salmon and other species as well as impacts on sacred places. The US tribes settled their claims with the federal government long ago. In the BC portion of the basin, the First Nations have neither ceded their rights nor made treaties. They often see the provincial government as a settler organization that is in direct competition with them for land and resources and cannot therefore credibly represent them. The federal government, which appointed itself in charge of the indigenous peoples and remains in this position of authority unless they assume self-government, is participating in consultation with First Nations, while BC is leading the planning for provincial negotiations as per the 1963 Canada–BC Agreement. The First Nations that assert rights in the Columbia basin are working to coordinate with the US tribes to identify common interests and convey to the BC government their concerns and hopes for improvements in the situation. The provincial government in turn is working to ensure that its consultation with basin constituents is comprehensive and inclusive as part of its preparation for Treaty negotiations by engaging Canadian First Nations on a government-to-government basis on the future of the Columbia.

CLIMATE CHANGE IMPACTS

In 1964, near the peak of post-war North American prosperity, political leaders were of course not yet aware of an already incipient major consequence of the Industrial Revolution. Today, we know that, due to unprecedented increases in carbon dioxide emissions from widespread use of the cheap power produced by fossil fuels, climate change now poses the threat of greater variability in basin flows than we have come to expect over the last 50 years. Scientists are using computers to construct downscaled climate models which translate large-scale trends into local impacts, based on current and projected global emissions and other current model assumptions. These downscaled models project significant shifts in the hydrological cycle in the coming decades. These changes include higher average temperatures, lower late-summer flows and warmer winters characterized by more precipitation falling as rain, as opposed to snow, which in tandem will result in changes in the timing and extent of peak flows. Recalibrating this balance will require new approaches to water governance that must be implementable in the next few years and must ensure we can continue to develop our adaptive capacity.

For example, we may need to enhance storage potential to capture winter rain that would once have run off in nature's convenient late spring melt gift to farmers and power producers alike. Climate change poses an increasing risk of severe and prolonged drought, which would profoundly reduce the electricity output of the system. And of course, power demand will increasingly escalate in summer for air conditioning and refrigeration, right when flows are at their lowest. One model produced by Dr. Alan Hamlet, formerly of the Climate Impacts Group at the University of Washington, projects a worst-case scenario of a 50 per cent drop in streamflow in the US portion of the basin by 2050. Farmers will need fresh water more than ever to help crops survive warmer and drier springs and summers. Experts warn of an impending global food crisis that will result from these same effects occurring elsewhere in the world, where resilience may be lower and resources scarcer. We can therefore speculate that the demand for and cost of food may rise, adding to the urgency of maintaining regional agricultural viability as the climate changes.

Ironically, the diametric opposite of drought is also a concern for the Columbia basin system. Increased storage capacity will be required for managing extreme rainfall events as well – what are called "cloudburst phenomena." With catastrophic floods experienced around the world in 2013 and again in 2014, the likelihood of a repeat of the Great Flood of 1894 seems ever greater, and we would do well to consider carefully the fact that mandated flood control under the Treaty ceases in 2024, to be replaced by "called upon" flood control. How will Canada manage storage in extreme precipitation events? To understand this conundrum one must envision the response mechanism: Canada would have to keep its storage drawn down in order to accommodate extreme flows. But if such flows do not materialize – and of course they are not entirely predictable – Canada must keep its storage levels up to offset the challenges to power generation and agriculture as outlined above and maintain its ecosystems in a healthy balance.

The challenge now facing the Columbia Treaty signatories on both sides of the border is to assess these risks and projections, find common ground on their separate goals and demands, and emerge with a modernized pact that has the capacity to respond to major climatic changes over time. It doesn't have to happen all at once, but provisions must be made to ensure the flexibility that will be required if we are to acknowledge and implement the adaptive advantage. In order to do this, though, the operating entities will need new, integrated models that assist decision-making by demonstrating the potential values of flows in a range of scenarios, and the impacts of reservoir management on those changing conditions.

Furthermore, these considerations must be interwoven with constructive approaches to the impacts outlined in this chapter to fish and other species, their habitats, residents of the basin in BC, and the Canadian First Nations and US tribes. In the next chapter, we explore the potential impacts of climate change on Treaty operations in more detail, and demonstrate how a changing hydrology and greater demands due to increased US populations and agricultural growth may influence the upcoming Treaty renegotiations.

Chapter Three

WHAT HAS CHANGED AND WHAT IS CHANGING

It is not always fair to judge the political and social conduct of one historical era by standards that predominate in a later one. Times change. In the case of the Columbia River Treaty, however, it is probably accurate to say that important downstream environmental and social costs were at best undervalued and in some cases ignored by the parties that crafted the final agreement. While the architects of the Treaty may be forgiven for not yet knowing the longer-term ecological impacts of dams on major river systems, the effects of large-scale blockages on salmon were already clearly understood. So too were the social impacts of the loss of salmon to the local indigenous peoples, who relied on the fish not only for food but also for spiritual inspiration. The effects of the construction of the Grand

Coulee dam, which began in 1933, had already provided ample evidence of all of these impacts.

It is difficult, therefore, to look back on the Columbia River Treaty – and how its terms and conditions were formalized – without at least a twinge of guilt over the fact that its provisions were clearly meant to ignore the pre-existing treaty entitlements and human rights of indigenous peoples on both sides of the international border they refer to as the Medicine Line. It is hard to imagine that the drafters did not recognize from the outset that by greatly diminishing the native peoples' principal natural food source, the dominant nations of the United States and Canada would be eroding one of the last pillars of indigenous self-determination and identity in the region. But the values of the day were such that economic progress was seen in elite circles to be more important than ecosystem protection and indigenous rights. Over the next 50 years, however, neither environmental issues nor social justice concerns would go away; rather, each passing decade simply put them into different but ever-increasing relief.

Faulty as the reasoning at the time may be perceived to be today, it appears it didn't have to be that way. Had it been decided, at the time, that social and environmental issues should be given equal weight, some of the serious environmental and social problems we face in the basin today could have been mitigated, if not largely resolved. Measures taken later, such as the enactment of endangered species legislation in the US in 1973 and the listing of Columbia salmon as endangered in 1991, were in part influenced by demands for the return of traditional access to salmon by First Nations in Canada and tribes in the US.

HOW DID ENVIRONMENTAL AND ABORIGINAL ISSUES GET SHORT SHRIFT?

As mentioned in chapter 1, important environmental considerations that would impact indigenous ways of life were expressly on the table in the initial reference from the Canadian and US governments to the International Joint Commission concerning what would become the Columbia River Treaty. The reference charged the IJC with determining whether, in its judgment, further development of the water resources of the Columbia basin would be practicable and in the public interest from the points of view of the two Governments, having in mind (A) domestic water supply and sanitation, (B) navigation, (C) efficient development of water power, (D) the control of floods, (E) the needs of irrigation, (F) reclamation of wet lands, (G) conservation of fish and wildlife, and (H) other beneficial public purposes.

Were the IJC to find that further works or projects were feasible and desirable, the reference further directed that it

should indicate how the interests on either side of the boundary would be benefited or adversely affected thereby, and should estimate the costs of such works or projects, including indemnification for damage to public and private property and the cost of any remedial works that may be found to be necessary, and should indicate how the costs of any projects and the amounts of any resulting damage [should] be apportioned between the two Governments.

The second-last instruction from the two governments was specifically technical, calling on the IJC to

> investigate and report on existing dams,
> hydro-electric plants, navigation works, and
> other works or projects located within the
> Columbia River system in so far as such in-
> vestigation and report may be germane to the
> subject under consideration.

The charge concluded by empowering the IJC, in conducting its investigation and otherwise performing its duties under the reference, to "utilize the services of engineers and other specially qualified personnel of the technical agencies of Canada and the United States" and enjoining it to

> so far as possible make use of information
> and technical data heretofore acquired by
> such technical agencies or which may be-
> come available during the course of the inves-
> tigation, thus avoiding duplication of effort
> and unnecessary expense.

Suddenly science was subtly subsumed under applied engineering. Today, of course, we realize that, because engineers, by virtue of professional ethics and standards of conduct, are so tightly focused on satisfying their clients, it is sometimes wise to provide outside scientific oversight and input into their decisions. But this was not how things were done at the time the IJC was charged with fulfilling the demands of the Columbia River Basin reference.

As these instructions appeared to carry a disproportionate amount of weight in the reference, it appears in hindsight that, in keeping with the political, economic and racial paradigms of the time, it could have been these instructions that in the end skewed the Treaty toward limited ends that underestimated environmental concerns and ignored the importance of salmon to the lives and livelihoods of indigenous peoples.

As noted earlier, it is important to bear in mind the historical character of the period. The reference to the IJC was made at the height of the Second World War, and the commission's consequent investigation and report were developed in the immediate post-war era when military and civil engineering were at last unleashed not in the service of warfare but in the immense effort to repair the damage and create a different and better future out of the most devastating conflict in all of humanity's history. Engineering and other applied sciences not only promised a world in which the ravages of the war could ultimately be forgotten, but a whole new world in which people could live better lives through rural electrification and work-saving new devices that had come into existence in large part because of rapid advancements in military technology and weaponry. That was the upside of the ijc reference.

The downside was that the reference also occurred at a time when warfare had altered more political boundaries than had ever changed over any other comparable period of time in the history of civilization. The West had prevailed, which meant that the governments of the US and Canada were breathing a sigh of relief and not thinking much about the rights of those who had been caught in the middle of these conflicts, nor of those whose rights and issues remained unresolved as a result of earlier conflicts associated with colonialism or other injustices perpetrated upon peoples who just happened to be in the way of imperialist interests. Nor were environmental concerns at the fore. Very few at the time even gave a moment's consideration to the fact that the Second World War had also caused more ecological damage around the world than any event of comparable duration in all of human history.

It would take a decade or two, but it was inevitable that an unbridled post-war focus on civil, mechanical, chemical and petroleum engineering advancements without a commensurate consideration of their ecological effects would eventually create environmental circumstances that would ultimately lead to serious problems. While a conservation movement had already existed in North America for decades, growing concerns over air and water quality and ecosystem decline stimulated the birth of a more highly energized and politically active environmental movement, not just in the US and Canada but globally. This movement was just gaining momentum at the time the Treaty was signed in 1961, however. Political realities with respect to the environment were only beginning to change when the IJC completed its study and made its recommendations.

WHAT GOALS GOT EMPHASIZED INSTEAD?

At the time, all evidence seemed to indicate that joint management of the system could have significant benefits for both nations. While the 1948 inundation of Vanport City, Oregon, occurred in a clearly identified floodplain in which the affected community should never have been located in the first place, it focused public attention in both countries on the value of the kind of flood protection only dams could provide. Rural electrification, which was occurring widely, demonstrated the extent to which both economic development and quality of life could be quickly enhanced through the benefits of hydro power generation. Reliable water supplies made possible by dams, especially the Grand Coulee, had already been shown to produce enormous benefits for irrigation agriculture in other parts of the United States. Thus, when the recommendations of the International Joint Commission were released in December 1959, the IJC proved it could certainly follow directions, or at least those that were writ large with respect to technical aspects of the reference with which they were charged. (The Treaty itself and various related texts were reprinted in 1964 as *The Columbia River Treaty Protocol and Related Documents*, listed in the Bookshelf section at the back of this volume.)

In March 1959 the Columbia River Engineering Board reported to the IJC, focusing on "the primary objective of producing the maximum feasible hydro-electric development of the Basin" in the context of a unified system which would with minor modifications also facilitate flood control. Although the scope of the report was basin-wide, it focused principally on larger developments of international significance on the main stem and major tributaries of the Columbia. It also noted that elements that were considered but found less desirable for inclusion in the hydro power and flood control plan receive full attention in the appendices of the report. The report went on to indicate that in accordance with the instructions of the IJC, no attempt was made "to apportion costs and benefits or indemnification for damages for specific projects between the two countries," but that facts and conclusions in the report could serve as a basis for recommendations to the two governments on these concerns. The Engineering Board report offered eighteen conclusions. Foremost among them was that further development of the water resources of the Columbia River Basin was practicable and in the public interest from the points of view of both Canada and the US. The three prominent areas of potential development were hydro power generation, flood control and irrigation. The conclusion that perhaps strikes us most as being different from what we might have arrived at today was this:

> (d) At present there is no urgent need for co-operative development in reclamation of wet lands and no reason for co-operative development in the fields of domestic water supply and sanitation, navigation or conservation of fish and wildlife.

It is with this conclusion that the preliminary thinking that would underpin the Columbia River Treaty wobbled off in a direction away from any rectification of the initial damage to salmon migration caused by the Grand Coulee dam, and this would in fact further prevent access by salmon to the upper part of the river. The issue would remain ignored until the United States passed endangered species legislation in 1973. As a result of this direction the existence of salmon would be threatened throughout most of the basin and deep injury caused to thousands of innocent people who had once relied on the species for subsistence. It was a direction that many of the architects of the Treaty would likely live to regret.

The fact that omitting consideration of potential impacts to fish and wildlife in the development of the Columbia basin was a faulty conclusion was not immediately apparent, at least to those who did not lose their homes and land or access to salmon. The Columbia was developed in an era when the building of big dams was held to be the fastest avenue to prosperity. While it was true that those dislocated by these projects often protested, it was also clear that the benefits of such structures and the electricity distribution systems that radiated outward from them far outweighed any social and environmental impacts associated with dam construction and reservoir development. It is important to recognize that these benefits are real and tangible. If tomorrow morning a choice came down to whether you had to put up with dams or live without electricity, most of the people who rely on the Columbia system for their power would not hesitate for a moment to make whatever trade-offs were necessary to keep their lights on. The "taming of the Columbia" also created a lot of well-paying jobs that generated, and continue to generate, a great deal of prosperity in regions that had been struggling economically. Our reliance on electricity has only grown since 1964. If anything has changed since then, it is not our reliance on hydro power but our understanding of the trade-offs that were required in creating the Columbia system, and what the ongoing trade-offs will be if we continue to operate the system as we have in the past.

DAMS: A 1970S GLOBAL MOVEMENT IN HINDSIGHT

We are hardly the first people to face facts related to the impacts of dams over the period of these developments' extended lifespans. Others around the world are asking many of the same questions that the people of the Columbia basin are wrestling with today as they confront the relicensing of

50-year-old dams and reconsideration of the half-century and older treaties that brought those dams into existence. The differences between what matters today compared to what mattered in 1964 can be seen in bold relief in the findings of the World Commission on Dams, which, in November 2000, published a report that famously allowed not just engineers but also members of civil society, academics, public and private sector interests and professional associations to offer perspectives related to the real and perceived benefits that accrue over time from large dams on major rivers. The report noted that dam building peaked in the 1970s when an average of two or three large dams were commissioned each day somewhere in the world. That era, however, has come to an end. Once considered unquestionable, the value of big dams in the context of expanded economic development is no longer perceived to be as black and white as it was in 1964. What is different between then and now is that, after damming half the world's rivers and building more than 45,000 dams of heights greater than four storeys, we are beginning to understand the full measure of these projects' social, economic and environmental impact.

The opening statements in the executive summary of the World Commission on Dams report could very well describe important elements of the debate over reconsideration of the Columbia River Treaty that is taking place on both sides of the border at the time of this writing:

> The global debate about large dams is at once overwhelmingly complex and fundamentally simple.... It is complex because the issues are not confined to the design, construction and operation of dams themselves but embrace the range of social, environmental and political choices on which the human aspiration to development and improved well-being depends. Dams fundamentally alter rivers and the use of a natural resource, frequently entailing a reallocation of benefits from local riparian users to new groups of beneficiaries at a regional or national level. At the heart of the dams debate are issues of equity, governance, justice and power – issues that underlie the many intractable problems faced by humanity.
>
> The dams debate is simple because behind the array of facts and figures, of economic

statistics and engineering calculations, lie a
number of basic and easily understood principles. If adhered to and routinely applied,
these principles would not only go a long way
towards responding to the controversy surrounding dams, but would markedly improve
decision-making on water and energy resources, achieving better outcomes....

The report goes on to express the commission's
overwhelming confidence in five findings. The
commissioners were of the view that there could
no longer be any doubt about the fact that dams
have made an important and significant contribution to human development and that the benefits
derived from them have been considerable. They
agreed, however, that in too many cases an unac-
ceptable and often unnecessary price has been paid
to secure those benefits, especially in social and environmental terms, by people displaced, by communities downstream, by taxpayers and by the
natural environment. They agreed also that a lack
of equity in the distribution of benefits has called
into question the value of many dams in meeting water and energy development needs when

compared with the alternatives. The commission suggested that the conditions for a positive resolution of competing interests and conflicts can be created by bringing to the table all those whose rights are involved and who bear the risks associated with different options for water and energy resources development. Finally, it was also noted that the negotiation of outcomes will greatly improve the development and effectiveness of water and energy projects by eliminating unfavourable projects at an early stage, and by offering as a choice only those options that key stakeholders agree represent the best ones to meet the needs in question. The world has changed, the commission concluded, and the direction in which that change is going is clear: in matters related to big dams the world is moving toward more thorough long-term analysis of environmental impacts; greater equity in decision-making; and a stronger focus on equity and social justice in situations of unequal power.

So what are the specific changes that have occurred in the Columbia River basin since 1964 that are substantial enough to demand attention in the above context in the reconsideration of the Columbia River Treaty?

1. We now recognize the harm that dams cause

Since 1964 enough time has passed to allow clear recognition and assessment of the long-term impacts of dams on river ecosystems. As the report of the World Commission on Dams points out, a useful indicator of the scale of human intervention in this regard is a recent estimate that dams, interbasin transfers and water withdrawals for irrigation have fragmented 60 per cent of the world's rivers. There is no question that in many cases dams have led to irreversible loss of species and caused significant damage to ecosystems.

The current state of scientific knowledge indicates that large dams have a range of mostly negative effects on ecosystems. Because ecosystem impacts vary regionally, it is difficult to precisely predict specific changes that are likely to result from the construction of a dam or series of dams. Based on the natural river regime and the geographical location of a given dam, however, it is possible to anticipate the type and direction of effects, with decreasing certainty from first- to third-order impacts.

First-order impacts involve the physical, chemical and geomorphological consequences of blocking a river and the alteration of the natural distribution and timing of streamflow, including, for instance, inundation of valley habitats and disruption of natural migration routes (also known as the "footprint" effect).

Second-order impacts involve changes in the primary biological productivity of ecosystems, including effects on riverine and riparian plant life and on downstream habitat such as wetlands, caused, for example, by fluctuations in reservoirs that are not natural for lakes that existed prior to storage.

Third-order impacts involve alterations to biota, such as fish species, caused by a first-order effect, such as blocking migration. Third-order impacts can also result from second-order effects, such as a decrease in the availability of plankton or other alterations of the food web. In addition, modifying the ecosystem can also cause changes in the biochemical cycle in the natural riverine system – for instance, changes in water temperature downstream of storages caused by the fact that most water is discharged from the surface level, which is warmer. Adaptive approaches to these impacts are being developed, such as lowering the position of intakes so that they draw subsurface water instead, thus cooling river temperatures downstream. These measures will become increasingly important as the quantity of glacial melt decreases along with its role as a thermal balance for the main stem Columbia.

We have also learned in the last 50 years that hydro power is not as green as we have been led to believe. Where reservoirs are not adequately cleared of vegetation before flooding, the decomposition of organic material over time can become a significant source of greenhouse gases. In studies of reservoirs in warm tropical countries, the amount of greenhouse emissions released as a result of organic breakdown was the equivalent of what would have been produced had the same amount of electricity generated by the dams in question been produced by coal-fired power plants instead.

Even in temperate regions, a lot of biological activity goes on behind dams. Because the natural flow of river sediments is halted by the dam, everything organic remains in a reservoir. Organic material blown in on the wind and the bodies of all the organisms that live and then die in the water accumulate as part of the sediments at the bottom of the reservoir. Decomposition of such creatures and other organic materials creates methane that builds up in the lakebed. Low oxygen at depth in the reservoir creates ideal conditions for the microbial activity that creates methane, and this appears to accelerate as the reservoir is drawn down over the course of the summer. A 2012 study at Lacamas Lake in Clark County, Washington, by Washington State University researchers Bridget Deemer and Maria Glavin demonstrated that the carbon storage capacity of reservoirs could be less than one-fourth of what was previously estimated, once the effects of drawdown were accounted for in emissions calculations – a particularly concerning issue for storage dams such as Grand Coulee, Mica and Koocanusa. The methane and CO_2 emissions resulting from this interruption of the downstream flow of organic carbon contribute to climate change.

As we have seen in the Columbia basin, efforts to counter the ecosystem impacts of large dams have had only limited success. In a chapter in *The Columbia River Treaty Revisited*, Chris Peery outlines the effects of dam and flow management on

Columbia River ecosystem processes. Dams and impoundments, and associated flow management, Peery points out, have had multiple direct and indirect impacts on ecosystem function in the basin. Dams that were built without fish passage continue to block access to 55 per cent of former spawning and rearing grounds for salmon. Even those dams that enable fish passage block the upstream movement of other important species, such as sturgeon. The flooding of valleys has eliminated complex river habitat such as meanders, side channels and wetlands and replaced them with slower-moving reservoirs. Flow regulation has disrupted the biological and physical connectivity of the water. It has been estimated that there was a 50 to 60 per cent decrease in average annual sediment transport to the estuary of the Columbia River between 1945 and 1999.

The dams have transformed the Columbia River into a series of slackwater lakes. Extremes of high and low water have been eliminated. Life-giving flood events known to be vital to the normal function of river systems have ceased to occur. As mentioned earlier, impounding of water behind dams alters natural temperature regimes in regulated river systems. Peery cites research showing that the mean maximum summer temperatures of water impounded behind dams in the basin have risen 1.8°C. Moreover, due to a changing climate, spring has advanced by 30 days and fall is delayed by 17 days. For many species, the Columbia basin is no longer the habitat it once was.

Peery is optimistic, however, that the trends related to reservoir management can be reversed through the use of new management tools such as the implementation of more natural flow regimes that allow controlled low-level flood events, and levee setbacks that enable more-natural channel development and riparian diversity. Peery maintains that people are part of the system and can do a lot to stem the loss of ecosystem function. Breakthroughs in ecological understanding of river system dynamics support this view.

2. We now recognize that natural ecosystems do more for us than we realized in 1964

A new and growing understanding of ecosystem dynamics centred on the nexus of water, food and energy has emerged in the last half century. We now realize that although the Columbia is a big system, it is not just its size that distinguishes it. It is also marked by its combination of latitude, longitude and altitude; rain and snowfall; the nature of its soils; the extensiveness of its forests and the coldness and cleanness of its waters. We now understand far better than we did in 1964 that the evolution of extraordinarily productive ecological circumstances in the Columbia basin is the result of synergy between ocean, atmosphere, land, water and rivers that have together, over millions of years, created what could be described as a veritable perpetual motion machine of energy and food production. Evidence of the productivity of this self-regulating, self-sustaining system is made visibly obvious by the largest salmon runs in the world. Estimates of the peak runs in the Columbia system prior to damming range from six million to as many as 16 million fish each year. We will never know how many salmon there really were, but we do know what the iconic fish symbolizes.

Salmon are electrons in the current of planetary life found at the nexus of water, energy and food in the Pacific Northwest. They are a species which transformed the enormous energy of the planetary cycle of ocean > land > life > water >

weather > climate, of which the Columbia is a regional expression, into bite-sized pieces that other life forms could metabolize. This is why, wherever we find salmon, we also find indigenous peoples whose cultural heritage has linked them directly to the ecological energy of the Columbia River for hundreds of generations. It was this globally significant energy system that was ignored and compromised in order to harness and control water in the Columbia River Basin. Because we did not have a full understanding of the riches we already had, we took one of the greatest natural ecosystem powerhouses on the planet and shut it down to produce electricity.

Dam construction caused convulsions throughout the entire natural energy cycle of the Columbia system. We realize now that we turned off our biodiversity-based planetary life support system function so that we could turn on our electric lights in the Pacific Northwest. There is an old joke told in business circles: "Want to know how to make a small fortune? Start with a big one." In ecological terms that's what we did in the Columbia basin. While no one would suggest that the dams and the electricity they produce are not important to our lives, new perspectives on ecosystem dynamics are likely to demand reconsideration of the purpose of the dams and the broader nature of the benefits that should be derived from their operation. At the time of this writing at least, such matters are difficult to discuss in the Columbia basin, in part because discourse related to the Treaty and the future of the larger basin has largely been dominated by those with technical interests who still wish to define the future by the technical and economic parameters established in 1964. It will be difficult to keep discussion over the future of the treaty at that level, however. Times have changed. Really changed. As a society, our values have been transformed in significant ways since those days. Not only are there new ways of estimating the economic value of environmental services, but there are also higher ideals to which we know we can aspire when it comes to transboundary agreements over water.

3. Fairness, equity and social justice matter more now than they did in 1964

A growing body of international example suggests it is important to break through half-century-old boundaries of thinking and look at a wider range of issues from different perspectives in reconsideration of the Columbia River Treaty. New attitudes, international standards and examples that focus on fairness, equity and social justice in matters related to the damming of transboundary waters have emerged that could guide energized deliberations on the future of the Columbia system.

The main principles embedded in international law include the need for greater local participation in basin-wide development; allocation of resources according to water rights rather than political and economic power; and the joint management of resources by all who share the basin. As part of decisions made with respect to Treaty reconsideration, outstanding social and environmental issues from existing dams should be addressed. Further development needs and objectives should be redefined through open and participatory processes that give social and environmental aspects the same weight as technical, economic and financial factors, so that significant impacts on threatened and endangered species and cultures can be avoided. Top-down, command-and-control decision-making should at all costs be avoided. Acceptance by the public should be demonstrated for all key decisions. This also means that decisions affecting indigenous peoples should only be taken with the free, prior and informed consent of those peoples. The implications of these new values in the context of reconsideration of the Columbia River Treaty are profound.

There is possibly no issue related to the negotiation and ratification of the Columbia River Treaty that has changed more in the legal and constitutional contexts of both countries than that of indigenous treaty and water rights. Aboriginal interests and rights were almost completely ignored in 1964, as noted in chapter 2. That is not likely to happen again. Co-operation, in the context of evolving international legal standards, implies that all key interests must be represented in collaboration over the management of shared waters. Changes in the Canadian Constitution since 1964 make it very clear that aboriginal peoples must be involved in the governance of the Columbia system and not just consulted as members of the public. This is not an argument from morality only; it is an established legal fact. First Nations in Canada are rights holders, not stakeholders, in the shared future management of the Columbia basin. While these new legal parameters trouble some people, others view this as an opportunity to reassess the relative value of traditional knowledge and to contrast its fundamental tenets as they relate to sustainability with those of modern Western science. This too is a domain that has changed considerably since 1964.

4. Traditional and local knowledge may be more valuable than we thought in 1964

Matters related to the meaning and relevance of traditional and local knowledge are coming to the fore more frequently now, particularly in discussions of what will ensure the sustainability of human existence in the Columbia basin most effectively over time. In these discussions there has been a great deal of debate about how traditional knowledge should be defined. Some take exception to the term "traditional," because to them it implies knowledge that is unsophisticated, archaic and out of date rather than being of use in contemporary society. Others take exception to the use of the term "indigenous knowledge," because they believe it excludes important local knowledge that is not embedded in the language and culture of a specific group. A generally accepted definition of traditional knowledge, in Canada at least, is one articulated by Fikret Berkes in her book *Sacred Ecology*, which focuses on traditional ecological knowledge and resource management. After much deliberation, Berkes defines traditional knowledge as "a cumulative body of knowledge, practice and belief, evolving by adaptive processes and handed down through generations by cultural transmission, about the relationship of living beings (including humans) with one another and their environment."

It is important to note also that there is a wealth of locally acquired knowledge among populations, irrespective of cultural or ethnic orientation, who live in close contact with the land, through agriculture, fishing or other land-based activities, and who have accumulated a lifetime of observations and experiences of a particular environment. What distinguishes traditional knowledge from this is the accumulation of understanding over many generations, leading to a broad and deep understanding of baseline conditions and patterns over time in a particular area.

Though such knowledge is timeless, the concept of "indigenous knowledge" or "traditional knowledge" has only recently become a part of scientific, academic and regulatory discourse about the governance of water. Such knowledge is increasingly seen as valid and has been shown to play an important role in modern environmental management and decision-making. As ethnographer, poet and linguist Robert Bringhurst pointed out in his book *Everywhere Being Is Dancing*, native knowledge, languages and cultures are a form of biodiversity.

When viewed from the context of the Western interpretation of the natural sciences, traditional knowledge is seen to be made up of a logical system of organized knowledge based on empirical data that draws on observations over time, and that historically has been codified and transmitted through oral narrative. Stories told by elders recount their personal experiences or those of their ancestors, while incorporating important information both about environmental elements and processes and about the underlying values or worldview that informs their interpretations of changes in the environment.

In 1964 it was widely held in places of political power that traditional knowledge was a form of misinformation, for which science was a cure. Today, however, traditional knowledge is increasingly seen as an alternative form of science in that it represents a kind of investigation that arrives by different means and avenues at the perception and expression of ultimate truths. As Bringhurst points out, it is only dogmatism – either religious or pseudo-scientific – that renders the relationship between these two ways of knowing contentious, causing one or the other to be driven underground.

Western scientists also are beginning to reach this conclusion. It is increasingly understood that, if traditional knowledge were reframed as a scientific experiment aimed at determining ways of extending sustainable human presence on this planet, it, as much as any similar experiment ever performed in the history of Western culture, would have to be deemed an unqualified success. Aboriginal peoples have managed to live sustainably in the Columbia basin for at least 10,000 years. Western efforts to achieve a similar duration of sustainable presence do not appear, at the moment at least, to hold similar promise beyond the undeniably valuable quality of life that we have achieved at the cost of our ecosystems' integrity, a side effect that many are now working to try to balance.

Traditional knowledge, Bringhurst reminds us, is really little more than a functioning community of stories that strives to maintain both its coherence and its relevance through constant and iterative retelling within a society over time. In this respect, mythology is similar to a living literary canon upon which a society constructs an ideological image of itself that can be subjected to slight but not fundamental changes in focus and intent in the midst of long-term change. The problem, however, is that the changes that are likely to affect indigenous and local ways of living in the Columbia basin most profoundly are not those of the incremental kind. It is now realized that the extent and rate at which hydro-climatic change is occurring in the northern hemisphere may make even the most enduring mythology difficult to sustain and embrace. If atmospheric warming continues at its current pace, the rate and extent of change may well undermine the foundation of the meaning and relevance of the traditional knowledge that currently exists. It may even undermine the possibility of traditional knowledge itself, at least as it is known presently.

One of the biggest changes that has occurred in our world since 1964, and one we cannot ignore in reconsidering the Columbia River Treaty, is the fact that our climate will never again be what it was then, at least not in any timeframe meaningful to anyone alive today.

5. Our hydro-climatic circumstances are changing

Some of the very best climate research in the world is being done in the Columbia basin. Research networks in both countries are creating future climate scenarios that will help characterize the kind of conditions to which the Columbia River Treaty will have to adapt in the future. One of the most important studies published in Canada on this topic is a report entitled "Potential Impacts of Climate Change on BC Hydro's Water Resources." The purpose of the study was to determine how future trends in climate might affect projected future reservoir inflows in three distinct regions of British Columbia critical to BC Hydro's generating capacity. These regions included the Upper Columbia basin, the Peace River region and the Campbell River basin on Vancouver Island.

In accordance with the United Nations Intergovernmental Panel on Climate Change, the authors of the report – Dr. Georg Jost, senior hydrologic modeller for BC Hydro, and Frank Weber, Hydro's highly respected runoff forecasting lead – define climate change as a change in the state of the climate that can be identified by changes in the mean and/or the variability of its properties, and that persists for an extended period, typically decades or longer. Climate change, they note, refers to any change in climate over time, whether due to natural variability or as a result of human activity. Jost and Weber then acknowledge that the recent warming trend associated with rising concentrations of greenhouse gases that trap heat in the atmosphere is taking place "at an unprecedented rate." They also note that "scientific evidence that this trend is partially caused by emissions produced by burning fossil fuels, and is likely to continue for many decades, is compelling." They also acknowledge that the current growth rate in actual greenhouse emissions globally is consistently at or beyond the worst-case scenarios projected by the IPCC.

Jost and Weber go on to list hydro-climatic changes that have already been observed in British Columbia. All regions of the province, they note, have become warmer by about 1.2°C on average over the past century. Annual precipitation has increased during that time by about 20 per cent, resulting in a modest increase in annual flows into BC Hydro reservoirs. That is what we have seen so far, but the future may be very different. Researchers with the Pacific Climate Impacts Consortium have projected that under most scenarios, extreme heat days in the basin could increase tenfold by 2050 and the number of extreme precipitation events could double or triple, with considerable impact on basin hydrology. As noted below, there is evidence now of a trend toward increasing intensity of extreme weather events.

What the authors of the BC Hydro report also noted was a clear recent trend toward decline in winter snowpack, which they attribute to natural climate variability. The report expressed concern, however, that the trend toward less precipitation falling as snow, rather than as rain, might continue under warming conditions in the future, further altering the timing, nature and extent of peak flows in the Columbia basin.

As is the case in many temperate-region basins around the world, snow storage is far larger than reservoir storage capacity in the Columbia basin. A snowpack's water content, Jost and Weber explain, is reported in millimetres of the equivalent amount of snow required to produce that water content. While the timing of peak accumulation can vary at individual locations, the date of April 1 of each year is used as a proxy for determining maximum snow accumulation during any given winter in the Columbia basin. A study of 73 sites in British Columbia revealed an average decline of about 18 per cent in winter snow accumulation across the entire province over the past 50 years. The distribution of this decline, though, was highly variable, ranging from 47 per cent in the middle Fraser River region, to 23 per cent in the Kootenays, to 20 per cent in the Columbia region, to almost no effects in the Peace River basin and in northern BC. The report attributes one-half to two-thirds of the reduction in peak snow water equivalent over the past 50 years to natural variability in the weather-determining ocean current cycles associated with the El Niño Southern Oscillation and the Pacific Decadal Oscillation. Researchers observed that, after removing the effects of this natural variability, changes in snow water equivalent in the winter snowpack throughout BC were in fact very small, perhaps as little as 4 per cent.

The researchers go on to acknowledge, however, a serious drawback in their snow water equivalent analysis which currently limits the potential usefulness of the technique, not just in BC and the Columbia basin but in every mountain region in Canada. The limitation is that most of the monitoring sites from which data were included in the analysis were located at mid-elevations, whereas models suggest that snow water equivalent may be increasing at higher, colder elevations. As noted earlier at page 39 some of these projections suggest that snow-water equivalent in the US part of the basin may decline by as much as 50 per cent in the coming decades. To their credit, Jost and Weber were also careful to acknowledge the limitations of their own modelling techniques. Global models, they explained, broadly reproduce historical climate at global scales but are less accurate at scales of less than several hundred kilometres, particularly in mountain regions like the Columbia basin, where effects are only roughly approximated. Complicated statistical algorithms can bridge the gap between global and regional climate impacts, but only at the price of higher degrees of uncertainty. The authors further caution that the absence of detectable trends in annual water supply should not be taken to imply there are none. The brief duration during which records of hydro-climatic parameters have been kept, and the sometimes poor quality of the data that is available, make it entirely possible that "a weak climate change signal could be hidden by more dramatic year-to-year fluctuations." There are other challenges as well. While the basic trends as modelled suggest higher inflows into all of BC Hydro's reservoirs, the models that currently exist have difficulty simulating evaporation and the response of vegetation, which are critical unknown factors in determination of climate change effects.

The models are limited in one other critical parameter. They do not attempt to simulate feedbacks in which changes in one hydro-climatic circumstance begin to cascade through others, such as when rising temperatures result in increased evaporation and a simultaneous increase in the amount of water the atmosphere can transport and turn into fuel for far more extreme storms. (It is a fundamental principle of atmospheric physics that a warmer atmosphere can transport greater volumes of water vapour.) As will be discussed in the next chapter, evidence suggests that far bigger precipitation events than have been experienced in the past are already making an appearance in the Columbia basin.

Another of the instances in which the climate change signal in British Columbia is not weak is in the decline of glacial ice. The BC Hydro report cites research conducted by the Western Canadian Cryospheric Network which demonstrates that glaciers in British Columbia lost about 11 per cent of their area over just the 20-year period between 1985 and 2005. Further research indicates that glacier cover in the Columbia basin declined by about 16 per cent in the 14 years between 1986 and 2000. This loss was insignificant, at least from the perspective of BC Hydro, since at the scale of the watersheds they manage, the impacts of glacial melt on annual reservoir inflows are relatively minor. Researchers Jost and Weber did acknowledge, however, that even though glaciers cover a relatively small area in any given watershed, they contribute significant flow in late summer. During the dry summer of 1998, for example, melt from glaciers that flow from the Columbia Icefield and elsewhere in the Columbia basin contributed 35 per cent of September inflows into the Mica reservoir (Kinbasket Lake). Simulations of changes in coverage project that glaciers will decline in area in the Mica basin by at least 44 per cent and perhaps as much as 100 per cent by 2100, with an average decrease of 85 per cent.

While cautious in its assessment of human-caused greenhouse emissions on overall precipitation patterns in British Columbia in the short term, the BC Hydro report was clear in its temperature projections for the next 50 years. The authors predict that, in general, the temperature trends observed over the past century in BC will likely persist throughout the 21st century, with the result that by 2050 we should expect all regions of the province to be warmer in all four seasons. Mean annual temperatures across the province are projected to increase by 1.4°C to 2.7°C. While average precipitation is expected to remain within the range of historical variability, these temperature increases are expected to create hydro-climatic extremes that are beyond the range of natural variability experienced by those living in the Columbia basin since climate record-keeping began. Some climate models suggest that in the Columbia Basin more disruption may be triggered by more frequent extreme events than by changes in seasonal weather patterns.

While it provides some very important current perspectives on the potential impacts of climate change on its own hydro power operations, the BC Hydro report is important also for its conclusions. It acknowledges that the 2012 report represents a start – but only a start – in its partnership with the Pacific Climate Impacts Consortium at the University of Victoria, upon whom the authors relied for much of the science undergirding the content of their report. BC Hydro acknowledged that it has not been determined how well reservoir storage will be able to buffer changes in seasonal runoff, such as lower summer inflows. The Crown corporation also needs to know a great deal more about how rising temperatures will affect heating and cooling demands in every region to which it supplies electricity. Much more needs to be known about how extreme weather events will affect the maintenance of Hydro's more than 56,500 kilometres of distribution lines and 18,500 kilometres of transmission lines. We also need to know more about how natural systems, including fisheries, will be affected by warmer temperatures. Just as important, we need better information about the demographic and socio-economic impacts that will follow in the wake of rising temperatures. The answers to all of these questions will have a bearing on the future practicality, functionality and ultimate acceptance of the next iteration of the Columbia River Treaty.

In the US, some of the most important projections related to climate effects on the future of the Columbia basin have been developed by the Climate Impacts Group (CIG) at the University of Washington in Seattle. Research findings based on the work of Dr. Alan Hamlet (mentioned in chapter 2) confirm those of BC Hydro and the Pacific Climate Impacts Consortium in Canada. The CIG projects that, in this century, the

Columbia basin will change from a snow-domi-
nated hydrological cycle to one dominated instead
by winter rains. Overall precipitation may not di-
minish, as BC Hydro has concluded, but more of
it is going to come as rain instead of winter snow.
Unfortunately, however, the results will be very
different in the US portion of the basin. While
the northern, Canadian, part of the Columbia basin is projected to lose little of its annual snowpack
and snow cover by the middle of this century, the
US portion could lose as much as 38 to 52 per cent
of its winter snowpack. These changes will disrupt
the timing of peak flows, the availability of water for irrigation and navigation, and hydro power
generation regimes throughout the entire, densely
populated lower part of the Columbia basin.

The growing realization of potentially deleteri-
ous effects of hydro-climatic change has been recognized on both sides of the border. But the two
countries do not appear to fully realize yet that it
is neither practical nor effective to address these
problems separately and independently. Under
such circumstances, it would appear inconceiv-
able that two nations with a 50-year history of
successful collaboration in the management of

their shared Columbia waters would abandon the Treaty that made that co-operation possible. Canada and the US share the Columbia basin, which means they have to manage it together. This realization alone should inspire co-operation instead of competition in reconsidering the Columbia River Treaty. At the time of this writing, however, full realization of what is at stake has yet to be acknowledged.

Chapter Four
WHAT IS AT STAKE

There is a great deal more at stake in negotiations related to the renewal of the Columbia River Treaty than is presently understood by the general public in either country. Of greatest importance would be the continuing effort to restore river ecosystem function that has been damaged or lost as a result of dam construction. Thus a primary goal of a renewed Treaty should be restoration of lost ecological elements and conditions that, 50 years later, are seen to be of far greater importance than the architects of the original pact were able to imagine.

The second thing a renewed Treaty could – should – do is redress injustices that today would be called human rights violations: consequences of the non-inclusive way the Treaty was negotiated and the final conditions that were imposed on those who were made subject to its terms. As

US author Helen Ingram has consistently asserted, no lasting settlement of water allocation is likely to be built on perpetuated inequity. Achieving equity, she argues, "requires sharing costs and benefits fairly, accommodating a plurality of values, establishing a widely inclusive political process, honouring social contracts and commitments and protecting the needs of future generations." As water scholar Paul Hirt demonstrates in his case study of rivers, hydro power and salmon in the Northwest, collected in the anthology *Water, Place and Equity*, river managers and developers in both countries have been violating each of these equity principles for more than a century. Not surprisingly, these perpetuated inequities have caused a great deal of social and political grief, beginning in the 19th century and evolving in a variety of ways after 1964 to the present day. This is why the First Nations that assert rights in the Columbia basin are working to coordinate with the US tribes to identify common interests and convey to the BC government their concerns and hopes for future improvements to the Treaty.

Also at stake is the ability of the people of the Pacific Northwest to monitor and respond to hydro-climatic change in the larger Columbia basin in a manner that will adequately permit coordination of effective and meaningful adaptation strategies. A renewed Treaty should lay the foundation for continuing improvement of social and economic resilience in the face of direct and indirect effects of climate change, not just in the basin but in surrounding regions as well.

The shared flood control and power generation benefits of the Treaty are founded on basic principles of co-operation and mutual interest. But today those benefits radiate outward to provide economic security and environmental and social stability to citizens of both countries in ways not foreseen when the Treaty was negotiated. It is these broader, unanticipated gains that are put into bold relief by climate change.

Recent analysis reveals that the Treaty provides clear advantages to both countries in terms of managing both present and projected climate change effects. Because negative effects – especially as they relate to water security – are likely to be more pronounced in the southern portion of the basin, the US stands to derive greater long-term value from perpetuation of a binational collaborative arrangement that assures basin-scale management of the Columbia River system. It is important to note, however, that while changing hydrological conditions in the basin may appear to offer relative advantages to Canada over the coming decades, these same conditions make it clear that continued co-operation in the management of the Columbia can be in the best interests of both countries.

From this we see that what is really at issue in reconsidering the Columbia River Treaty is nothing less than the region's real prosperity, however you want to define that concept. At stake is not just a substantial amount of revenue, and savings such as the avoided costs of flooding, but also what money itself does and what it ultimately represents in any given region over the long term. There are sound economic reasons for improving on the initial terms and conditions of the Treaty. The authors of this primer and members of the Adaptation to Climate Change Team (ACT) at Simon Fraser University have examined five such benefits. While all of the economic numbers included below are preliminary and provisional, they point to the fact that more work needs to be done to clarify the current and growing economic value of the advantages that accrue to the people of the Pacific Northwest from the Treaty they have largely taken for granted for the past 50 years.

1. Flood control is more valuable than ever

The abstract of the 1959 report of the International Columbia River Engineering Board to the IJC offered some very interesting observations about flood control in the Columbia basin. The report noted that "early basin-wide floods caused comparatively little damage" because economic development was small at the time. However, as development in the region has progressed and large areas of flood plain have become occupied, potential damage from basin-wide floods has increased correspondingly. The report noted that the flood of record, which occurred in June 1894, produced a maximum discharge estimated at 0.68 million cubic feet per second at the international boundary and 1.24 million cubic feet per second at The Dalles dam, which spans the Columbia at the boundary between Washington and Oregon. At peak flood stage at The Dalles, the Columbia was flowing 34 feet above extreme low water and 26.6 feet above the mean annual flow. The report also noted that the US Army Corps of Engineers had estimated that between 18 and 21 million acre-feet of additional usable storage capacity would be required to control a flood of the magnitude of the 1894 one down to 800,000 cubic feet per second at The Dalles, which in the Corps's estimation would eliminate all major damage in the lower reaches of the river.

As described earlier (see page 18), the US paid Canada $64.4-million to provide 8.45 Maf of flood storage under a plan that specified guaranteed reservoir levels and capacity as well as additional storage on an on-call basis. The amount paid represented half the estimated value of the damage that would be avoided by Treaty flood control from 1968 through 2024. Due to population growth, urban development and the expansion of irrigation agricultural land – all of which were made possible by the Treaty's success – the actual value of the flood control Canada has provided to date is likely at least an order of magnitude greater than this amount.

It is in the domain of flood control that the Columbia River Treaty may well be most valuable to the US in the context of future climate change effects on the hydrology of the region. While many still tend to think the future is going to be more or less the same as the past, everything we know about the effects of warming on water and the hydrological cycle suggests that one of the things we can expect to be very different in the future is the frequency and magnitude of storms.

The US was among the first countries in the world to figure this out. A report by their National Research Council in 2011, *Global Change and Extreme Hydrology: Testing Conventional Wisdom*, confirms how serious the loss of hydrologic stationarity could be in North America and around the world if current trends persist. The NRC's findings include consensus on the fact that a warmer atmosphere will carry more water vapour, which will result in more frequent and far more intense extreme weather events. The report concludes by pointing out that continuing to assume stability in the hydrological cycle in designing and operating water management systems "is no longer practical or defensible." What this means is that the old math and the old methods may no longer work.

Scientific attention focused on atmospheric dynamics has revealed some very interesting phenomena related to how much water vapour a warmer atmosphere may be able to transport. Satellite remote sensing has revealed the presence of what are being called atmospheric rivers, moisture-laden currents of air aloft that have likely existed for an eternity. Atmospheric rivers appear to begin as narrow streams of hurricane-strength winds that fill up with water vapour as they cross warm ocean waters. They become corridors of intense winds and moist air that can be 400 to 500 kilometres across and thousands of kilometres long. When these rivers of water vapour are drawn inland, they precipitate nothing less than what can be described as a deluge. A single atmospheric river can carry the equivalent of 10 times the average daily discharge of the St. Lawrence River. It appears that the flooding in the Kootenay–Columbia region in 2012 was caused when an atmospheric river deposited 250 to 500 millimetres of rain in mountainous regions, resulting in flash flooding in the town of Sicamous, fatal landslides at Johnson's Landing and altered operations at BC Hydro dams at Revelstoke, Kinbasket, Arrow and Duncan. At Castlegar the storm broke the previous precipitation record by 87 per cent.

The fact that the Columbia River Treaty came into existence largely as a result of the devastation caused by the flooding of Vanport City, Oregon, in 1948 will not be lost on US negotiators. Nor will the now widely recognized fact that for every dollar spent on flood protection, communities can expect to avoid at least five dollars in damage. Recent devastating floods in both Canada and the United States remind us also that the public can lose confidence in government agencies that fail to properly protect people from flood damage. Given that the value of flood protection is widely accepted, it would be political and legal suicide for US negotiators to reduce their own flood protection capacity by abandoning agreements with Canada to provide carefully coordinated upstream storage.

We have also learned that, given the expanded economic and societal value of what it protects, flood control today is worth orders of magnitude more than in the past and far, far more than when the Columbia River Treaty was signed 50 years ago. It is precisely in order to quantify this increased importance of flood protection that the Adaptation to Climate Change Team is

undertaking a study of the exact value of the infrastructure and built environment that is shielded
by the Treaty today as compared to a half-century
ago. It is hoped that the results of this study will
help put into relief the relative value of flood protection to both countries.

2. Drought management

Some areas of the Columbia basin are already dry
and drought prone. All climate change models
project that drought will occur more frequently
throughout the Pacific Northwest region. Basin-
scale co-operative management of the Columbia
system is the only way the growing spectre of deep
and persistent drought can be effectively managed
to the optimal benefit of both countries. As noted
in chapter 3, climate researchers are predicting significant differences in the depth and duration of
snowpack and snow cover, particularly in the US
portion of the basin. The holding back of water
supplies in the Canadian portion of the basin to
compensate for this shift in the delivery of fresh
water to the landscape and its ecosystems could
take enormous pressure off the US to build expen-
sive additional storage in a part of the basin where

few desirable reservoir sites remain, yet more will be needed.

As we'll see next, the value of coordination with respect to drought management can be calculated, and such assessments demonstrate that this type of co-operation will be essential to the sustainability of agriculture in the basin on both sides of the border, but particularly in the US.

3. Sustaining productive irrigation

Economist Joyce Yuan, a member of the Adaptation to Climate Change Team, conducted a study using data from 72 counties in Washington and Oregon to project the cost of climate change to irrigated agriculture. The work utilized the observed effects of reduced runoff during the low-snowpack years of 1992 and 2001 as potential models for future climate impacts and assumed there would be proportional reductions in surface water availability for irrigation as a result. The study concluded that annual damage to irrigation agriculture in the US part of the basin would range from $465-million to $2.4-billion. The width of this range resulted from using various scenarios for snowpack reduction (50, 60 and 70 per cent) and various prices of water ($50, $100 and $150 per acre foot). Given that US irrigators are currently paying as much as $200 per acre foot, the study's estimates are conservative.

Taking into account the reported conditions of climate change and current average water prices in the Columbia basin, Yuan estimated that the loss to irrigated agriculture during an extended drought would be between $1.43-billion and $2.29-billion. It is important to note that this loss merely indicates the cost to government to maintain a certain level of irrigation given the effects of decreased snowpack runoff; it does not take into consideration potential temperature or precipitation changes. Clearly, co-operation on basin-scale management of the Columbia system will be required to mitigate impacts on irrigation agriculture in the US portion of the basin.

4. Salmon and other ecological values

The protection of natural ecosystem function and the restoration of salmon to those parts of the Columbia basin where they have been eliminated by dams can only be accomplished through the high level of mutual trust and co-operation made possible by a formal treaty between the two nations. Further research by Joyce Yuan has established that the value of "natural infrastructure" is being recognized on both sides of the border. Her work revealed that roughly five million households, or at least 15.09 million people, have a personal stake in the Columbia basin. Related studies have found that the annual mean household willingness to pay to preserve an ecosystem in a river basin similar to the Columbia is $252. If this number is accurate, the minimum publicly perceived annual benefit of the ecosystem services provided in the Columbia basin would amount to somewhere between $327.6-million and $1.26-billion annually. These services include ecosystem benefits such as water purification by wetlands and riparian habitat, soil retention, carbon sequestration and storage, and the existence value of unaltered ecosystems.

In addition, it has been shown there is a willingness to pay for the protection of salmon habitat on the part of users and non-users alike (that is, people who fish recreationally or for sustenance, and people who don't fish at all). The range of this willingness to pay is estimated at $26.52 to $74.16

per person annually, which translates to roughly $421.7-million to $1.18-billion per year for the Columbia basin. In terms of protection of wildlife habitat, the annual willingness to pay has been shown to be about $69.30 to $117.86 per person, or $1.1-billion to $1.87-billion annually for the entire basin. Effectively organized international co-operation therefore appears to have the potential for extensive public support.

5. Power generation and the Canadian Entitlement

Joyce Yuan also initiated a study on the impacts of climate change on energy production. Due to uncertainties in the primary data (mostly to do with global climate models and electricity pricing), quantifying these effects for the Columbia basin will require more calibration to reflect current conditions. Existing data, however, suggest that, on average, there will be a $437-million loss per year compared with hydro power production in the current climate regime. This number is based on a study done for Great Lakes hydro power generation as roughly adjusted to reflect the production capacity of hydro plants in the Columbia basin. Again, although this estimate offers a general idea of the economic impact climate change may have on energy production, it does need to be refined in order to improve its accuracy. The point remains that we need to better understand the economic value of meaningful co-operation.

Even though preliminary, these estimates also demonstrate how complicated the issue of the Canadian Entitlement has become. What is clear, however, is that the mutual value of mitigating climate change effects on the severity of drought, reducing the spectre of diminished agricultural productivity and managing the increased threat of extreme weather and flood events must all be taken into account in the calculation of the Entitlement. Suffice it to say that collaboration on ecosystem values should form part of the broader renegotiation of the future relationship between Canada and the United States with respect to shared responsibility for the Columbia River system.

Chapter Five

WHAT ARE THE PROSPECTS FOR RENEGOTIATING THE TREATY?

As noted earlier, 2014 is the earliest year when either government can officially notify the other concerning the potential to end the Columbia River Treaty. In theory, there are three options for reviewing the pact:

1. An agreement to let the Treaty expire in 2024. International logistics for managing the international waterway would be subject to the general provisions of the Boundary Waters Treaty of 1909 and to international law. It is likely the parties would agree to maintain some provisions of the original Treaty.
2. The parties could give notice of termination but then decide to renegotiate the whole Treaty from scratch. Given the length of time it took

to craft the original agreement, the greater complexity of the issues and the demands of the general public, interest groups and First Nations, it is unlikely the Treaty could be renegotiated within 10 years.

3. Retain the Treaty but renegotiate some of its provisions and operating procedures. This is the so-called "modernization of the Treaty" option.

Both entities have signalled in their reports to their respective governments that they prefer option 3. However, there are significant differences in their approaches to the scope of the issues that will be negotiated starting in 2014.

Both governments and their respective Treaty entities are undertaking extensive consultations with numerous interests and have established various organizations to assist them in these discussions. The initial consultations extended over two years, with draft reports issued during the summer of 2013 and final reports submitted near the end of the year.

GOVERNANCE IN TRANSITION

Before we explore the nature and content of the consultation undertaken by both the Canadian and the US entities, it is worth reiterating three overarching governance factors that have shaped the evolution of the Treaty over the past 50 years for which we have laid out the case in this primer.

1. Increased concern over ecosystem health

The original Treaty was essentially a commercial agreement on power and flood control that gave scant attention to ecosystem values. Over the past decades, this imbalance has changed dramatically, especially in the US, where a series of laws and agreements have been instated to protect flows and habitat for migrating salmon. On the Canadian side, there is concern about the effects of fluctuating reservoir levels on resident fish and wildlife. In 1991, migrating salmon in the Columbia basin were officially listed under the US Endangered Species Act of 1973. This was followed by a series of agreements and protocols under the Treaty to establish fish conservation flows in the Columbia and adjust storage releases to protect fish. In BC this increased focus on ecosystem values was manifested in a Fish and Wildlife Compensation Program, funded by BC Hydro, that was established in 1995 to mitigate some of the impacts of reservoir flooding. In addition, the water licences for the Columbia Treaty dams in Canada were amended in the first decade of the new century to rebalance flow releases for power and for ecosystem values under water use plans.

2. Consultation with First Nations and the public

As noted, there was little or no engagement with affected parties during the final negotiations for the Treaty between 1960 and 1964. Neither the First Nations in Canada nor the tribes in the US were meaningfully consulted. This was partly because, in Canada, although First Nation rights to the lands they used and occupied pre-existed European Contact and were acknowledged under the Royal Proclamation of 1763 (engaging what is called "the honour of the Crown" to deal fairly with the First Nations), these rights were not formally entrenched, with a duty to consult, until sections 25 and 35 of the Constitution Act, 1982 came into force.

Renegotiation of the Columbia Treaty will now be based on a model of collaborative, rather than top-down, governance on both sides of the border. The consultation process that is outlined in this chapter attests to this new reality. It also means that the scope of discussions during the renegotiation of the Treaty over the coming decade will be much more complicated than the original approach, with a much wider array of values in play.

3. Changing climate and hydrology

As noted in earlier chapters, climate and hydrology were not issues in the public mind at the time the original Treaty was signed. Over the past decade, however, changes in temperature, hydrology and the frequency of extreme events – both flooding and drought – have been extensively studied by scientists. The Columbia River Treaty renegotiation will hopefully lead to the pact becoming one of a number of modern international river basin agreements in which climate change has played a significant role in the design of treaty outcomes.

CANADIAN CONSULTATIONS AND POSITION

The government of British Columbia is to take the lead in Treaty consultations in preparation for 2024 and to keep the federal government informed. BC consequently established a Columbia River Treaty Review Team within its Ministry of Energy and Mines, which conducted several rounds of consultations in 2012 and 2013 with a wide range of interest groups and community associations in most of the towns in the Columbia basin. It also undertook government-to-government discussions with the First Nations as required by the Canadian Constitution, whereby impacts of any changes to the Columbia Basin Treaty on First Nation rights and title must be consulted on and accommodated. The team undertook three rounds of consultations, mostly in the Kootenay Region, over two years.

The issues raised in these consultations can be organized into the following categories:

1. ecosystems, including salmon restoration, on the main stem of the Columbia;
2. flood control and the Libby Coordination

Agreement, which pertains to the operation of the Libby dam;

3. power generation and the Canadian Entitlement;
4. socio-economic issues such as recreation, economic development, agriculture, transportation;
5. climate change adaptation; and
6. principles.

1. Ecosystems

Principal concerns in this category focus on the effects of fluctuating reservoir levels on fish and wildlife habitat, agriculture and riparian vegetation. Feedback from the public showed appreciation for two BC government initiatives in this regard. The first of these, established in 1995, is the Columbia Basin Fish and Wildlife Compensation Program. Funded by BC Hydro with revenue from the Canadian Entitlement, the program is intended to mitigate impacts of the original flooding by Treaty dams on fish and wildlife populations and habitats. There were concerns that impacts on fish and wildlife in Canada caused by the Libby dam were not adequately compensated, and the program has now been extended to the Koocanusa reservoir as well (see also next, under "Flood control").

The second initiative that found favour with the public is the Water Use Plan for the lower Columbia, undertaken in 2007 as part of Hydro's province-wide effort "to find a better balance between competing uses of water, such as domestic supply, fish and wildlife, recreation, heritage, and electrical power needs, which are environmentally, socially and economically acceptable to British Columbians." This plan is constrained by the provisions of the Treaty, however.

Generally, Canadians feel the US should fully support any costs associated with return of salmon into the main stem of the Columbia, and that Canada should only become engaged in feasibility studies of salmon returning if the US makes it possible for fish to navigate the major barriers that have been erected in the US portion of the basin.

In summary, at the time of this writing in early 2014, Canadians are more interested in terrestrial ecosystem enhancements than are Americans, who thus far have tended to focus more on aquatic ecosystems.

2. Flood control

Most residents support the current, coordinated flood control measures under the Treaty, which led, for example, to the successful management of extremely high water in the spring of 2012. They are skeptical that the mandated change in the flood control agreement scheduled for 2024, which shifts from joint coordination of all reservoirs to called upon flood control as explained in chapter 1 (at page 23), would be in the best interests of both parties. There is strong desire in Canada to balance flood control with ecological management in order to ensure that regulation of reservoir levels respects the functionality of riparian ecosystems. There is particular concern over the operation of the Libby dam and Koocanusa reservoir, as the Libby Coordination Agreement, negotiated by the parties outside the Treaty, is not seen to be working to the benefit of local BC residents, who experience wide fluctuations in the reservoir's levels. They feel that this situation will only get worse under called upon flood control, and that the effects of a changing climate on water needs south of the border will only exacerbate these challenges.

3. Hydro power and the Canadian Entitlement

Most residents strongly believe that the Canadian Entitlement is the only benefit Canada receives from the Treaty, but they have differing opinions on its role in a modernized Treaty. Some think there should be a reduction in power-related flow releases to the US in order to protect ecosystem values in Canada. Others feel that the funding from the Entitlement should be increased and a portion of the additional money applied to maintenance of aging Treaty infrastructure. Still others believe the US should be paying for additional benefits they derive from having a secure water supply for agriculture and communities, flows for salmon, and improved navigation.

4. Socio-economic factors

Residents of the Canadian part of the Columbia basin are somewhat resentful that the Entitlement payments go directly into general provincial revenue. Many feel that insufficient funds are directed toward managing regional Treaty storage issues such as loss of agricultural lands and production, particularly in the face of a climate future where local food supplies may become even more valuable. Other effects criticized include disruption of transportation infrastructure, affecting forestry and communities; fluctuation of reservoir levels, which has effects on water-based recreation; and the fact that grants paid by BC Hydro to local government in lieu of taxes are often perceived as inadequate. Some basin residents are pressing for an Environmental Entitlement that would compensate for ecological damage and fund restoration.

5. Adaptation to a changing climate

Residents are acutely aware that basin hydrology is already shifting in its timing and flows as a result of the changing climate. The Columbia Basin Trust has funded studies for a number of basin communities on climate adaptation, all of which have pointed to increases in the frequency, severity and duration of extreme weather events such as heavy rain and drought.

6. Principles

These widespread public consultations have resulted in the Columbia River Treaty Review

Team identifying the following set of principles for its recommendations to the provincial government:

- Ongoing impacts of the Treaty in BC must be explicitly recognized.
- All downstream benefits to the US due to co-ordinated operations – flood control, hydro power, water supply, navigation, fisheries – should be accounted for and their full value shared between the two countries.
- Planning of operations should be coordinated to maximize benefits to both countries.
- British Columbia will seek improved coordination in Libby dam and Koocanusa reservoir operations.
- All operating conditions of BC dams will be subject to provincial and Canadian law, to water use plans where they exist, and to consideration of aboriginal rights.
- Treaty provisions after 2024 should be flexible enough to allow for continuous adaptation to climate change as the challenges evolve over time.
- Adaptation to climate change should also

be incorporated into Treaty planning and implementation.

- Implementation of called upon flood control measures after 2024 should be undertaken only where there is an extreme risk of flooding and the US has made effective use of its own storage facilities first before seeking additional help from BC.
- Ecosystem values are an important factor in implementing a modernized treaty, and BC will seek to improve ecosystem health both within and outside of the Treaty.
- Salmon migration in the main stem of the Columbia is not a Treaty requirement, and each country should be responsible for restoring fish passage as feasible with regard to their respective infrastructure.
- The province will continue to consult with First Nations and communities throughout the renegotiation process.
- Columbia basin issues not covered by the Treaty will be addressed through other government programs and initiatives.

In preparation for its brief to the provincial

government, the Treaty Review Team drafted a report in June 2013. An overview of the Treaty and a commentary on the draft US position paper were released that same month, which we will have more to say about below.

The main point in the report is that the nature of the Canadian Entitlement has changed significantly since the Treaty was ratified. The Canadian entity releases water at the border in compliance with the operating plans under the pact, and originally most of those regulated flows were used to generate electricity, for which the province received annual payments of between $100-million and $300-million. Over the years, the US entity has broadened the use of this regulated water for other purposes, notably for fish flows in the main stem Columbia to meet the requirements of the US endangered species legislation for migrating salmon; to secure water supplies for irrigated agriculture and urban development; and for maintenance of water levels in the lower Columbia for navigation (up to 60 per cent of US wheat exports travel through Columbia river ports).

In addition, the report points out that the changes in climate that have been modelled to date (as mentioned in chapter 4) indicate that annual inflows to the Canadian portion of the basin will likely increase, though seasonality of flows will change, while net inflows south of the border will decrease. Accordingly, it is in both parties' best interests that the collaborative arrangements in the Treaty should continue, albeit modified, to the optimum benefit of both countries.

US CONSULTATIONS AND POSITION

The US entity undertook a similarly comprehensive consultation, establishing a Sovereign Review Team comprised of representatives from the four Northwest states, 15 tribal governments and 11 federal agencies. Supporting the review team is a Sovereign Technical Team, responsible for undertaking technical assessments in support of the Sovereign Review Team and the US entity.

The main issue of contention in the US to date is the value of the Canadian Entitlement. As mentioned earlier, the Entitlement is calculated on a complex theoretical formula established at the time of the Treaty negotiations, based on half the additional value of power to the US that can be created by the regulation of Treaty dams in Canada. The US entity considers that the amount of money paid by 2024 will have fully compensated Canada for its infrastructure under the Treaty, and that operation of US storages is now constrained by requirements to meet fish flows under US law enacted after the Treaty was negotiated. The current formula for calculating the Entitlement lapses in 2024 and will therefore be a significant factor in the negotiations over the coming decade.

The US believes that the value of power post-2024 should be based on the difference between coordinated and uncoordinated cross-border hydro operations. Their initial estimate of this difference is $26-million annually, or about 10 per cent of the Entitlement payments under the current formula. As noted in the section on Canada's position above, Canada believes flood protection has been undervalued and that there is a basket of water security benefits gained by the US in addition to power production – fisheries, water supply and navigation – all of which will become more valuable over time as water supplies diminish in the US portion of the basin under a changing climate and growing population.

The US entity released its recommendations to the Department of State on December 13, 2013. As is the case with Canada, the US entity supports a modernized Treaty over either terminating the pact or renegotiating it from scratch. However, the US entity and the Sovereign Review Team place increased emphasis on ensuring healthy and more resilient ecosystems together with continued management of flood risk and assured hydro power production. The central focus of the US position is to reduce the financial cost of the Canadian Entitlement and reallocate some of those funds to ecosystem restoration, meeting flow requirements for migrating fish and securing water supplies for agricultural and municipal use in the face of a changing climate.

Principles

Like the Canadian side, the US entity bases its recommendations on a set of general principles:

- Seek the greatest possible shared benefits to both countries for a wide range of economic, community and ecological benefits.
- The health of the Columbia ecosystem

should be a shared benefit and cost to both countries.

- The minimum duration of the post-2024 Treaty should be long enough to provide sufficient long-term assurances of beneficial outcomes, but adaptable enough to allow responses to new information and changing conditions.

- All operations should be informed by science and as far as practicable be based on measurable outcomes.

- Operations should meet all applicable US laws and regulations, especially recognizing tribal treaties and rights.

- Both parties should pursue more coordinated use of Treaty and Canadian non-Treaty storage to meet a range of outcomes.

- The strategy for adapting the Treaty to future changes in climate should be resilient, adaptable, flexible and timely as conditions warrant.

- US interests should ensure that future costs associated with any Treaty operation are aligned with the appropriate party.

- Implementation of ecosystem-based functions should be compatible with rebalancing the Entitlement and reducing US power costs.

1. Hydro power

The US position is that the Canadian Entitlement should be based on half of the actual benefits received in the US from coordinated operations, as compared to non-coordinated operations. As mentioned above, the US entity calculates this benefit to be around $26-million per year, compared with up to $300-million per year under the current formula, a full order of magnitude less. The US is also concerned about reliability of the system in relation to shifts in streamflow quantity and timing as a result of climate change.

2. Flood control

The US seeks assurances that the level of risk associated with the called upon flood control provision after 2024 will be the same as that in the current Treaty. The US also wants to negotiate conditions for the use of called upon flood control, namely that it occur only when coordinated Canadian water releases do not provide sufficient storage in conjunction with the full use of US system flood storage or when needed during refill season to modify planned Canadian releases. Future planning should also take climate change into account, both for the prospect of more extreme wet weather events and for potential drought years, to protect ecosystem function.

3. Ecosystems

The US entity places renewed focus on protecting streamflows and habitat for migrating and resident fish. They wish to undertake a joint program with Canada in this regard and share the cost of implementing fish passage to Canadian spawning grounds. A modernized Treaty should also minimize adverse effects on cultural resources important to First Nations in Canada and tribes in the US. There is common agreement to improve operation of the Libby dam to provide mutually desirable ecosystem benefits to both sides of the border.

4. Water supply

More emphasis is placed on providing water for irrigated agriculture as an important authorized purpose, through Canadian storages. This additional demand has to be balanced with protecting ecosystem function and water rights, including tribal reserved water rights.

5. Navigation

The regional and national significance of Columbia River navigation has increased significantly over the past 50 years. Hence, the US also wants to designate maintenance of water levels for navigation as an authorized purpose.

6. Climate change

As is the case with Canada, the US is aware of the potential impacts of a changing climate on all authorized purposes of water and seeks to improve the science and understanding of this change on operational systems. They include a call for collaboration with Canada on sharing science and data.

ANALYSIS OF THE CANADIAN AND US POSITIONS

Both the Canadian and the US entities met their primary obligations to advise their respective governments on their interests for a post-2024 Treaty in December 2013. In their conclusions, it is clear that there is mutual interest in modernizing the pact using its existing framework rather than ending it or attempting to renegotiate it.

Both countries believe there is more to be gained through coordination of the current storage infrastructure, and that there needs to be more emphasis on supporting healthy ecosystems in addition to the economic values associated with flood control, power, agriculture and navigation. In short, a modernized Treaty will be as much about water security as about hydro power generation and flood control.

Both parties are also vitally concerned with the prospect of a changing climate affecting the volume and timing of flows throughout the Columbia system. Both would agree to monitor this over time and share ongoing studies into modelling how the hydrology will change on both side of the border and what flexibility will be required, both in operational arrangements and in the timing of any formally renewed agreement after 2024.

However, there are also clear differences in position, particularly over the appropriate value of the Canadian Entitlement and the desire to return migrating salmon to the entire Columbia system. How the parties will approach their similarities and differences over the coming 10 years is the subject of the final chapter of this primer.

Chapter Six
WHAT'S NEXT?

There have not yet been any formal negotiations between the two parties as at the time of writing, in 2014. All of the consultation has occurred on each side of the border by each of the two entities, their constituents and First Nation and tribal representatives.

Now that both parties are aware of each entity's recommendations and underlying principles, there will undoubtedly be further analysis of critical issues over the coming months by the respective entities to prepare for negotiations.

As noted in previous chapters, the Columbia Treaty has evolved over three stages. The first stage covered the period from the mid-1940s to the ratification of the Treaty in 1964 and was dominated by a strong engineering focus with priorities fixed in economic outcomes for flood control and hydro power. There was little empathy expressed for the rights of First Nations and tribes, nor for disruption of communities by reservoir development in Canada, nor for loss of valuable ecosystem resources.

The second phase covered the period from about 1973, when the final two dams were completed, to the present. A number of developments occurred during this time: reasonable attempts were undertaken to mitigate the major environmental impacts associated with restoring fish passage in parts of the Columbia; numerous projects were implemented to improve fish and wildlife habitat in the Canadian portion of the river; there were attempts to achieve a better balance between power production and ecology through the Northwest Power and Conservation Council; and similar modifications were made to the operation of Canadian storages to provide some relief for resident fish populations below the major dams.

In addition, there has been formal recognition of the rights and title to water and resources that First Nations hold in British Columbia and the beginning of meaningful consultation with them on

Treaty renewal and their interests in the upcoming negotiations by the BC government. Though these talks do not compensate for the wrongs that were inflicted on indigenous peoples on both sides of the border under the original Treaty, there is at least the start of a respectful dialogue that augurs well for the next stage.

The start of formal negotiations between the two governments will usher in the third phase of the Treaty. Now the parties will have to address a much wider array of values. They will be required to continue meaningful engagement on both sides of the border with public interests, local governments and First Nations and tribes, and deal not only with the growing uncertainties posed by a changing climate and hydrology but also with challenges to water security arising from a growing range of authorized uses.

In short, it is a whole new ball game, one that will test the notion of integrated watershed governance in the 21st century. It also has the potential to set an example for the rest of the world on enlightened management of issues associated with international water treaties in a changing climate.

INTERNATIONAL PRACTICE FOR RIVER BASIN MANAGEMENT IN A CHANGING CLIMATE

Adapting to a changing climate is becoming a feature of other international basin agreements and treaties and is now a major concern for trans-basin planners and policy makers. Lawyer and ACT researcher Melissa Kruger examined some of these international treaties to see how they have dealt with the prospect of a changing climate.

The jurisdictions that have most successfully incorporated meaningful climate change provisions into international agreements are those that have overarching joint governance over the entire basin and where legal flexibility is built into their amending procedures. Given the shared principles for addressing climate change in the recommendations of both Columbia Treaty entities, it appears likely that the modernized agreement will include greater recognition of changing climate and hydrological regimes.

For example, amendments to existing agreements for the Rio Grande and Colorado rivers and the Great Lakes to accommodate adaptation to climate change are broadly consistent with the mechanism in the Columbia River Treaty that enables amendments by way of diplomatic notes. The broadest use of diplomatic notes is set out in Art. XIV(4), which provides that "Canada and the United States of America may by an exchange of notes empower or charge the entities with any other matter coming within the scope of the Treaty."

Further legal work is required in order to determine whether the scope of the current Treaty is sufficiently broad to address climate change and whether the pact's protocol procedures allow the entities to incorporate new commitments to address this concern.

MODELLING AND ECONOMIC ANALYSIS

Forecasts of how Columbia basin hydrology will be affected by a changing climate will be a critical feature of the coming negotiations. Both governments have initiated new research into hydrologic modelling to build on the work undertaken to date as described in chapter 4. The Canadian initiative is led by the Pacific Climate Impacts Consortium (PCIC), located at BC's University of Victoria. PCIC will develop the "Variable Infiltration Capacity" hydrologic model (originally devised by researchers at the University of Washington for the US portion of the basin) for the entire basin, and will include new procedures designed to calculate the effects of glacial melt on streamflow and water temperatures. The updated forecasts are expected to be completed by the summer of 2015.

In the US, the Bonneville Power Administration has also contracted two modelling teams, from the University of Washington and Portland State University, to develop alternative forecasts for the entire basin. Both teams will use multiple hydrologic models and two methods for downscaling global climate projections to the Columbia basin region. They also plan to include a glacial melt model. These three teams are not working in competition, however; indeed, they met in January 2014 to compare early results from their modelling and continued to share information over the ensuing months. The purpose of exploring the various models is to understand what kinds of differences may exist in forecasts using different parameters, and thereby obtain a more robust set of scenarios of potential ranges of flows over the coming decades.

It should also be noted, however, that these models are generally based on average conditions and are not able to forecast extreme events that may be associated with increased atmospheric water vapour and other processes. Notwithstanding this caveat, both parties will have access to improved, comprehensive analyses of potential changes in hydrology. All three research groups will be simulating unregulated streamflows. These will then have to be routed through the operating models, which include reservoir storage. The range of regulated flows from various climate scenarios and hydrologic models will be used by both entities to prepare their respective positions on supplies of water, seasonality and the increased range of demands for water supply, navigation, flood control, power production and fish and other ecosystem needs. This new analysis is scheduled to be completed by the summer of 2016.

British Columbia's focus will likely be on a more robust and comprehensive analysis of the potential economic values associated with the widened range of authorized uses. The preliminary economic assessments mentioned in chapter 4 will be buttressed by more in-depth economic analyses. It is clear that the entitlement for augmented flows across the border will become more broadly based than simple power values. Likewise, the change to the called upon flood control arrangement to replace the current formula will require sophisticated modelling of potential flood flows in the US portion of the basin before there is a further need to require Canada to modify its storages to provide additional capacity in extreme flood events.

The very preliminary analysis by ACT researcher Joyce Yuan outlined in chapter 4 indicates that there are large and real values attached to water security in the US that warrant increased investment in calculating these values in advance of negotiations.

The hallmark for both parties will be certainty in the face of an increasingly uncertain future. Allocation of waters in the Columbia provides a wide array of goods and services, but these benefits show less and less value the more uncertain they become.

This third stage of the Columbia Basin Treaty will certainly prove to be the most interesting and challenging phase to date of this landmark international transboundary water agreement.

WHAT IS AT STAKE BEYOND THE COLUMBIA BASIN?

It is clear to many observers that the Columbia River Treaty could become the first transboundary water agreement in the world to be effectively reformed so as to create a living blueprint for how people would like to live in the Columbia basin, and basins like it, now and in a sustainable future. What is at stake, finally, is our moral duty.

The reconsideration of this Treaty provides an opportunity to show the world how to shed the limitations of the past in ways that will allow others to use our example to break out of the prisons of treaties that no longer address the realities they face nor confront the new challenges that are emerging as the global hydrological cycle responds to a rapidly warming atmosphere.

As Yakama tribal elder Gerald Lewis pointed out at a conference on the Columbia River Treaty in Ellensburg, Washington, in 2012, we have to keep in mind that we are not reconsidering this

Treaty just to satisfy ourselves. We are doing this for future generations.

Angus, David Grogan. "Valuing Ecosystem Services in the Salmon River Watershed, British Columbia: A Choice Experiment Approach." Master's thesis. Vancouver: Simon Fraser University School of Resource & Environmental Management, 2012. Accessed 2014-05-25 (pdf) from http://summit.sfu.ca/item/12452.

Berkes, Fikret. *Sacred Ecology: Traditional Ecological Knowledge and Resource Management*. Philadelphia: Taylor & Francis, 1999.

Bringhurst, Robert. *Everywhere Being Is Dancing: Twenty Pieces of Thinking*. Kentville, NS: Gaspereau Press, 2008.

The Columbia River Treaty, Protocol and Related Documents. Ottawa: Government of Canada, Departments of External Affairs and Northern Affairs & Natural Resources, February 1964. Accessed 2014-05-28 (pdf scan) from http://is.gd/ZcsK3n.

Constitution Act, 1982, being Sched. B to the Canada Act 1982 (UK), 1982, c. 11, ss. 25, 35. Accessed 2014-08-01 at http://can-lii.ca/t/ldsx.

Cosens, Barbara, ed. *The Columbia River Treaty Revisited:*

Transboundary River Governance in the Face of Uncertainty.
Corvallis: Oregon State University Press, 2012.

Demuth, Mike. *Becoming Water: Glaciers in a Warming World.*
Calgary: Rocky Mountain Books, 2012.

Gleick, Peter. "Whose Water Is It? Water Rights in the Age of
Scarcity." Posted to the *SFGate* (*San Francisco Chronicle*)
blog *City Brights* August 2, 2009. Accessed 2014-06-28 at
http://is.gd/WPueVf.

Goodstein, Eban, and Laura Matson. "Climate Change in the
Pacific Northwest: Valuing Snowpack Loss for Agriculture
and Salmon." In *Frontiers in Ecological Economic Theory and
Application*, edited by Jon D. Erickson and John M. Gowdy,
c. 10. Cheltenham, UK: Edward Elgar Publishers, 2007.

Harden, Blaine. *A River Lost: The Life and Death of the
Columbia.* New York: W.W. Norton, 1996.

Hirt, Paul W. "Developing a Plentiful Resource: Transboundary
Rivers in the Pacific Northwest." In *Water, Place and Equity*,
edited by John M. Whiteley, Helen Ingram and Richard
Warren Perry, c. 6. Cambridge, Mass.: MIT Press, 2008.

Jost, Georg, and Frank Weber. "Potential Impacts of Climate
Change on BC Hydro's Water Resources." BC Hydro
GDS12-324. Vancouver: BC Hydro, n.d. Accessed 2014-05-
28 (pdf) at http://is.gd/2l2NsY.

Loo, Tina. "People in the Way: Modernity, Environment
and Society on the Arrow Lakes." *BC Studies* no. 142/143
(summer/autumn 2004): 161–196. EBSCOhost document
16284786 (pdf) accessed 2014-03-28 via proxy server (consult your local public library).

Loomis, John, et al. "Measuring the Total Economic Value of Restoring Ecosystem Services in an Impaired River Basin: Results from a Contingent Valuation Survey." *Ecological Economics* 33 (2000): 103–117. Full text (pdf) accessed 2014-05-25 at www.msu.edu/user/lupi/aec829/D.pdf.

MacDonald, R. St. J. "Charles B. Bourne: Scholar, Teacher and Editor, Innovator in the Development of the International Law of Water Resources." *Canadian Yearbook of International Law* 34 (1996): 3–88, at subhead "Bourne and the Columbia River Dispute": 46–55.

McBean, Gordon, and Dan Henstra. *Climate Change Adaptation and Extreme Weather*. Vancouver: Simon Fraser University Adaptation to Climate Change Team, 2009. Full text (pdf) accessed 2014-05-25 from http://act-adapt.org/extreme-weather.

National Research Council. *Global Change and Extreme Hydrology: Testing Conventional Wisdom*. Washington, DC: The National Academies Press, 2011. Full text accessed 2014-05-25 at www.nap.edu/openbook.php?record_id=13211.

O'Riordan, Jon. *Climate Change Adaptation and Biodiversity*. Vancouver: Simon Fraser University Adaptation to Climate Change Team, 2009. Full text (pdf) accessed 2014-05-25 from http://act-adapt.org/biodiversity.

O'Riordan, Jon, Erik Karlsen and Bob Sandford. *Climate Change Adaptation and Canada's Crops and Food Supply: Background Report*. Vancouver: Simon Fraser University Adaptation to Climate Change Team, 2013. Full text (pdf) accessed 2014-05-25 from http://act-adapt.org/food-supply.

Olsen, D., J. Richards and R.D. Scott. "Existence and Sport

Values for Doubling the Size of Columbia River Basin Salmon and Steelhead Runs." *Rivers* 2, no. 1 (1991): 44–56.

Peery, Chris. "The Effects of Dams and Flow Management on Columbia River Ecosystem Processes." In *The Columbia River Treaty Revisited: Transboundary River Governance in the Face of Uncertainty*, edited by Barbara Cosens, 138–174. Corvallis: Oregon State University Press, 2012.

Pentland, Ralph, and Chris Wood. *Down the Drain: How We are Failing to Protect Our Water Resources*. Vancouver and Berkeley: Greystone Books, 2013.

Sampson, Bruce, Linsay Martens and Jeff Carr. *Climate Change Adaptation and the Low Carbon Economy in BC*. Vancouver: Simon Fraser University Adaptation to Climate Change Team, 2010. Full text (pdf) accessed 2014-05-25 from http://act-adapt.org/low-carbon-economy.

Sandford, Robert William. *Climate Change Adaptation and Water Governance*. Vancouver: Simon Fraser University Adaptation to Climate Change Team, 2011. Full text (pdf) accessed 2014-05-25 from http://act-adapt.org/water-security.

———. *Cold Matters: The State and Fate of Canada's Fresh Water*. Surrey, BC: Rocky Mountain Books, 2012.

———. *Restoring the Flow: Confronting the World's Water Woes*. Surrey, BC: Rocky Mountain Books, 2009.

———. *Saving Lake Winnipeg*. Surrey, BC: Rocky Mountain Books, 2013.

———. *Water, Weather and the Mountain West*. Surrey, BC: Rocky Mountain Books, 2007.

Sandford, Robert W., and Merrell-Ann S. Phare. *Ethical Water: Learning to Value What Matters Most.* Calgary: Rocky Mountain Books, 2011.

White, Richard. *The Organic Machine: The Remaking of the Columbia River.* New York: Hill & Wang, 1995.

World Commission on Dams. *Dams and Development: A New Framework for Decision-Making.* London, UK, and Sterling, Va., USA: Earthscan Publications Ltd., 2000. Full text (356 pp., pdf) accessed 2014-05-25 at http://is.gd/tiQQmY.

The RMB manifestos

PASSIONATE. PROVOCATIVE. POPULIST.

RMB has created one of the most unique non-fiction series in Canadian publishing. The books in this collection are meant to be literary, critical and cultural studies that are provocative, passionate and populist in nature. The goal is to encourage debate and help facilitate positive change whenever and wherever possible. Books in this uniquely packaged hardcover series are limited to a length of 20,000–25,000 words. They're enlightening to read and attractive to hold.

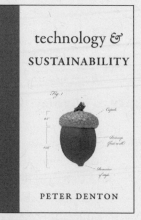

technology &
SUSTAINABILITY

PETER DENTON

ISBN 978-1-771600-39-2

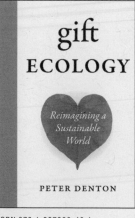

gift
ECOLOGY

*Reimagining a
Sustainable
World*

PETER DENTON

ISBN 978-1-927330-40-1

ISBN 978-1-771600-36-1

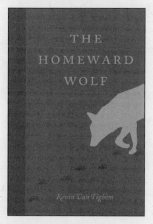

ISBN 978-1-927330-83-8

ISBN 978-1-771600-04-0

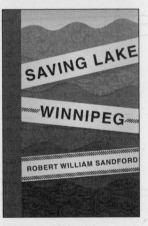

ISBN 978-1-927330-86-9

ISBN 978-1-926855-70-7

ISBN 978-1-897522-61-5

ISBN 978-1-897522 10-3

ISBN 978-1-926855-72-1

ISBN 978-1-927330-80-7

ISBN 978-1-926855-68-4

ISBN 978-1-926855-58-5

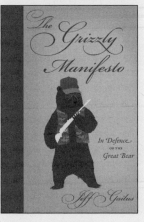

ISBN 978-1-897522-83-7

ISBN 978-1-926855-67-7

ISBN 978-1-926855-65-3

ISBN 978-1-927330-89-0

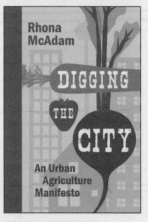

ISBN 978-1-927330-21-0

RMB saved the following resources by printing the
pages of this book on chlorine-free paper made with
100% post-consumer waste:

Trees · 6, fully grown

Water · 2,760 gallons

Energy · 3 million BTUs

Solid Waste · 185 pounds

Greenhouse Gases · 509 pounds

CALCULATIONS BASED ON RESEARCH BY ENVIRONMENTAL DEFENSE AND
THE PAPER TASK FORCE. MANUFACTURED AT FRIESENS CORPORATION.